PROBLEMS IN
Small Boat Design

PROBLEMS IN
Small Boat Design

Selected from the papers of
The Society of Small Craft Designers

Introduction by Gerald Taylor White,
Chairman, SSCD

ILLUSTRATED WITH PLANS AND DRAWINGS

1972
SHERIDAN HOUSE · NEW YORK

FOREWORD

WITH the rapid increase in boating interest on the part of the American public, there has come an awareness on the part of boat owners, and the boating industry in general, that even the simplest power or sailing boat represents considerable in the way of engineering. The same thing applies to those who are purchasing their first craft; at least some knowledge of the sort of engineering that went into the design is of great help before the investment is made.

All boat owners cannot, of course, be naval architects or members in the Society of Small Craft Designers. On the other hand, safety and economy during operation must by their very nature be important to the men who turn to boating for their pleasure or who are engaged in any phase of the boating industry.

Since the founding of the Society of Small Craft Designers in 1949, more and more interest has been evidenced in the technical papers that are inevitably a part of the Annual and Chapter meetings of the Society. These papers have been published in *The Planimeter* that goes to all members of the Society each month, but they have not until now been available to the general public.

At the 1957 Annual Technical Meeting of the Society,

it was voted that some of the papers be assembled into a volume that would be of great value on the book shelves of all members of the boating industry as well as all boat owners who are more than casually interested in the sport. Sheridan House was contacted and the present volume is the result. The papers are all by leading professional naval architects specializing in the boating field and the selection was made so that even the man who is not technically trained will find, several, if not more of the articles of great value.

In offering this book to the public, the Board of Governors of the Society of Small Craft Designers offers sincere thanks to each of the individual authors for their cooperation and to Member Tom Davin for his efforts to so successfully attend to the multitude of detail involved.

THE BOARD OF GOVERNORS,
The Society of Small Craft Designers, Incorporated
GERALD T. WHITE, *Chairman*

CONTENTS

8   *Contents*

PROBLEMS IN
Small Boat Design

Chapter One

MOTORSAILERS

By JOHN G. KINGDON

TWO types of cruising yachts were developed rapidly
after the advent of the internal-combustion engine—the
straight power cruiser and the auxiliary. The former
is wholly dependent upon its engine or engines and is
therefore completely helpless if it runs out of fuel or has
mechanical trouble. And, lacking the dual dampening influence of wind on sails and water on sizable keel, it rolls
and pitches much more violently in a seaway than does
an auxiliary.

These disadvantages aren't particularly important in
protected waters, but are magnified to matters of prime
importance when the power cruiser pokes her nose into
the open sea. It isn't advisable to take many such boats
offshore except for limited periods of time.

The auxiliary has neither of these faults, but is still far
from being the ideal ocean going cruising yacht. It is
designed for high efficiency under sail alone, so it is
rather slow under power. Because of its narrow beam and

long ends, which are necessary for speed under sail, its below-deck living space is small when compared to that of a power cruiser of the same over-all length. And the usual auxiliary, with its exposed steering position in the open cockpit, furnishes the helmsman little or no protection from the elements.

Thus it was inevitable that a third type of cruising boat be born—a boat whose lines would be right for proper speed under power, yet one that would have the ability to sail. This type, which came to be called the motorsailer, wasn't developed overnight. The yachting journals of 15 to 25 years ago carried frequent discussions as to just what a motorsailer should be. Some designers and yachtsmen insisted that the type should be able to sail just as fast as it could go under power.

Gradually, however, the following definition, composed by a well-known yachting writer a few years ago, came to be generally accepted: "If a boat goes faster under sail than under power, then she's an auxiliary cruiser. If she goes faster under power than under sail, then she's a motorsailer."

The late William H. Hand, Jr., noted designer and authority on motorsailers, agreed with this definition and elaborated a bit when he wrote: "While the standard auxiliary employs sail as primary driving power with the engine secondary, the motorsailer reverses this practice, the engine being primary and the sails secondary.

"The motorsailer has good speed under power, performs quite well under sail alone, and, when cruising under both sail and power, has the 'feel' and easy motions of a sailing craft rather than the quick, uneasy motions of a motor cruiser. And, if properly designed, built and equipped, it is a real seagoing craft, capable of going anywhere at any time.

"I have owned and cruised in every type of craft and believe the motorsailer to be by far the best development to date. It's without equal for the owner who likes a man's boat with real seagoing qualities."

Because Mr. Hand stressed seagoing ability so much, the typical Hand motorsailer was ketch rigged, rather heavily built, and had great stability, a long cruising range, and a maximum of comfort on extended trips. To eliminate all the scrubbing and polishing necessary on boats with a lot of mahogany, the cabin exterior was painted. Teak was used for the main deck, the outside trim, and the hatches. The interior was usually white pine with black-walnut trim.

From what Mr. Hand said about performance and motion in a seaway, it should be evident that you can't take the average power cruiser, add a small jib and mainsail, and call the result a motorsailer. Despite the fact that the engine is the primary means of propulsion, as long as the hull is that of a power cruiser no amount of sail will make a motorsailer out of her.

The true motorsailer has certain definite characteristics that set her apart. First, she has a long, straight keel, which gives great stability with moderate draft. The stability should be sufficient to allow carrying all working sails in winds up to, but not including, gale force. The light draft lets one poke around inland waters where the typical deep sailboat cannot navigate.

Second, she has a sail area that measures 60 to 70% that of the usual auxiliary of the same size.

Third, she is customarily ketch rigged.

Fourth, she usually has a deckhouse and can be steered either from this shelter or, like the auxiliary, from a position just forward of the rudder post.

Many motorsailers are fitted for offshore fishing, a job where their size, stability, and hull form are perfect.

That the type need not be especially slow under sail was proven by Gordon Munro in the motorsailer *Harbinger*. Her measurements are: 35′ 0″ overall length, 31′ 6″ waterline length, 10′ 0″ beam, and 5′ 11″ draft. She carries 680 sq. ft. of sail. An unusually fast boat for her type, she once traveled for hours on end under sail alone at better than 8.25 knots. That this is fast becomes apparent when it is realized that the maximum theoretical speed of a sailboat 31′ 6″ on the waterline (1.4 times the square root of the waterline length) is 8.41 knots. In all fairness, it should be pointed out that *Harbinger* has a speed-length ratio (speed divided by the square root of length) of 1.47, which is somewhat higher than the generally accepted figure of 1.3 for motorsailers.

A study of the midship sections shown on the accompanying drawing should clarify the basic differences between the motorsailer, the auxiliary, and the power boat. Depicted are *Harbinger*, a power boat having an overall length equal to *Harbinger*'s, and an auxiliary having a waterline length equal to *Harbinger*'s. The power cruiser's measurements are 35′ 0″ overall length, 33′ 4″ waterline length, 10′ 10½″ beam, and 2′ 10″ draft. With two 110 hp engines, she cruises at 18 mph. The auxiliary's measurements are 45′ 6″ overall length, 31′ 6″ waterline length, 11′ 0″ beam, and 6′ 10″ draft. A jib-headed yawl, she is exceptionally smart to windward in rough going despite the fact that she was not designed primarily for racing. *Harbinger* has a midship section coefficient of .49 compared to .66 for the power boat and .43 for the auxiliary. *Harbinger's* midship section area is 22.24 sq. ft., while that of the power boat is but 8.56 sq. ft. and that of the auxiliary is 26.24 sq. ft.

Besides the usual working sails, the motorsailer because of her stability is admirably suited for carrying a variety of light sails. For jogging directly down wind, twin spinnakers can be spread. On other points of sailing, such sails as a balloon jib and a big fisherman can be used to advantage.

Appended to this paper are two tables. The first lists in detail the design characteristics of a 65 ft. motorsailer of recent design. The second is a tabulation of the general characteristics of a number of motorsailers.

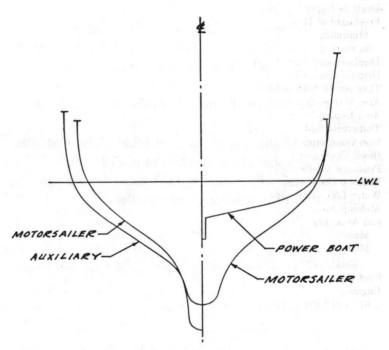

Fig. 1. Midships section of the 35 ft. motor sailer "Harbinger," a 31 ft. 6 in. w.l. auxiliary; and a 35 ft. l.o.a. power boat.

KETCH-RIGGED MOTORSAILER

Length Over All..............................	64' 11"
Length Water Line...........................	58' 2"
Beam..	15' 7"
Draft.......................................	5' 3"
Draft to Rabbet.............................	4' 4½"
Freeboard at Bow............................	7' 6"
Minimum..................................	4' 1"
at Stern..................................	5' 2"
Displacement, Salt Water....................	31.2T
Displacement, Fresh Water...................	36.35T
Tons per Inch Immersion.....................	1.38T
Area Wetted Surface.........................	876.6 sq. ft.
Area Lateral Plane..........................	266 sq. ft.
Transverse BM...............................	.676
Fuel Consumption............................	0.43#/b. hp/hr.
Block Coefficient...........................	.37
Prismatic Coefficient.......................	.55
Midship Coefficient.........................	.67
Water-Line Coefficient......................	.71
Midship Area................................	40.1 sq. ft.
Sail Area, Jib..............................	205 sq. ft.
Main....................................	595
Mizzen..................................	265
Total...................................	1,065 sq. ft.
Fuel Capacity...............................	640 gal.
Engine......................................	Winton 6-179

6½" x 8½" 150 b. hp.@ 850 r.p.m.

Table I

MOTORSAILERS, GENERAL CHARACTERISTICS

LOA	LWL	B	D	Weight Tons	Rig	Sail Area	Horse-power	Speed	Ballast
23' 9"	19' 9¼"	9' 2"	3' 0"	2.68	Sloop	350	25	9 mph	1,300 lb.
25' 11"	22' 6"	8' 4"	2' 9½"	3.54	Sloop	305	25	7 K	1,680 lb.
30' 0"	27' 6"	9' 6"	3' 3"	5.75	Ketch	260	50	8 K	7,000 lb.
30' 0"	28' 0"	10' 0"	4' 0"	8.00	Sloop	482	8 to 10	7 mph	3,215 lb.
33' 9"	30' 0"	11' 0"	3' 8"	7.81	Ketch	356	40	11 mph	9,200 lb.
35' 7"	32' 1"	9' 8"	4' 4"	9.46	Ketch	515	40	9 mph	14,800 lb.
44' 0"	40' 0"	12' 0"	5' 6"	18.08	Ketch	741	36	8 K	7,200 lb.
44' 9"	35' 0"	11' 8"	5' 0"	13.00	Ketch	645	55	9 K	3,360 lb.
45' 0"	41' 6"	12' 6"	4' 9"	18.75	Ketch	592	80	8 mph	7,000 lb.
48' 6"	43' 0"	12' 0"	5' 0"	17.60	Ketch	924	40	10 K	
54' 5"	48' 10"	15' 5"	5' 9"	34.00	Ketch		200		
64' 11"	58' 2"	15' 7"	5' 3"	31.20	Ketch	1065	150	10½ K	
66' 9"	56' 6"	16' 0"	5' 0"	33.00	Ketch	1300	120	9 K	16,800 lb.
70' 0"	52' 0"	15' 0"	7' 0"	34.70	Ketch	1333	72	9 K	
78' 0"	68' 6"	16' 0"	6' 6"	45.00	Cutter	1685	66		
80' 0"	68' 0"	18' 8"	7' 0"	90.00	Ketch	1700	300	12 mph	31,000 lb.
100' 6"	93' 10"	21' 0"	9' 0"	130.30	Ketch	2507	340	10 K	33,600 lb.

Table II

Chapter Two

THE MONOHEDRON HULL

By LINDSAY LORD

IT was back in the rum running days when the planing hull really began to prove its worth as a fast load carrier. It pounded in choppy seas and its heavy weather gyrations were only for desperate men fleeing from the law. The design of these boats was based largely on a strong V-bottom hull capable of floating two Liberty engines. That kind of power handled the weight of several hundred cases of what the labels proclaimed as ancient Scotch and the hulls lifted out fairly well and planed.

But as old George Owen, sailboat designer extraordinary and professor of Naval Architecture used to snort: "Put that power on a barn door and it would plane."

On duty again in World War II, the planing hull reappeared in a big way. PT boats powered with three Packards sped through the over-heated imaginations of publicity men in excess of 50 or even 60 knots. But other than as enlistment bait, the Navy found little real use for its potential stingers. Whole squadrons spent the entire war period on practice maneuvers only.

In the first place, they were too slow. No PT with full equipment ever touched 40 knots and therefore they had to avoid Jap destroyers. But most disappointing of all was their inability to go out in anything but moderate seas and not pound themselves helpless.

As constant and repeated repairs were made to these boats, in their own yards located beyond the fringe of high brass observation and interest, it developed that changes and experiments could be made and nobody higher up seemed concerned. Whole new bottoms shaped to reduce pounding and increase the lift, radical departures from the master blueprints in BuShips sacred files, were apparently of interest only to those immediately sticking out their necks for sweet science.

The term "monohedron" was finally coined to indicate the type of bottom which these PT experiments gradually evolved. It means a geometric shape whose running lines are presented at a single plane angle to the water. It was not a new discovery. There had been previous hulls with parallel, or nearly parallel buttock lines. Yet while these constant sections were no novelty, no program of experiment had ever been undertaken to make full scale comparisons of performance between constant section and warped plane types, between wide and narrow planes and among these planes with varying entrances and load factors, all under deep sea conditions.

Two years of these comparisons, using several squadrons of boats for testing, conclusively revealed that, given a non-pounding entrance, the monohedron hull eliminated transient suctions and uncertain pressure patterns below the working plane. With reduced suction, net lift improved with some benefit to speed and considerably increased load carrying ability. By shortening and widening the plane, lift efficiency was further improved. But these tests were all made on hulls of PT size and fitted with 4,500 horse power.

Since the war a great many monohedron hulls have been built in every country. For the most part these hulls have been small pleasure and fishing vessels with a minimum of power, as befits the usual private owner today and the results achieved suggest that a significant fraction of the world's floating equipment is still not covered by existing data. Classification of this particular fraction is not easy since dimensionless ratios are not wholly applicable throughout the range.

In the slower types, Taylor's standard series, while extending as high as speed-length ratio 2, are obviously of little use above speed-length ratio 1.3 since his parent forms are now no longer used for speeds above this ratio, particularly in small craft. For hull forms in the planing range, no ratio based on length has constant value.

However, in the range between S/L ratio 1.3 and, say, 2.2, the small craft designer finds himself most frequently occupied. In this range the phenomenon of planing action begins and may materialize in greater or lesser degree. Below this range the hull is purely a displacement form and above, planing action may be presumed to be fully developed.

Tests with the monohedron in this intermediate range

indicate that prior to full planing, such a hull fails to develop a speed-power relationship in keeping with a fair extension of the same curve as it plots above the minimum range of full planing. To make the curve fair in this intermediate range, a monohedron bottom must be somewhat modified toward the double wedge form. That is, the running lines must display a slight upward slope from the deep forefoot. They may retain some parallelism among themselves but not with the static water line.

In this zone between two types of hydrodynamics, the monohedron in any form retains to some degree one of its most interesting characteristics which is the quality of dynamic stability. Pressure taps installed through the bottom over the whole plane area indicate that the monohedron constant section bottom develops a relatively stable pressure pattern which holds true even down into speeds where only the tendency to plane exists. It is this stable pattern of positive pressures which give the monohedron its stability in confused seas and adds to its freedom from broaching in following seas.

Further modification may be warranted under certain conditions when comparisons are being made with the typical warped plane type, under calm water conditions at moderate planing speeds. Here, the warped plane's tendency to squat, is, like a hooker of whiskey, stimulating before it becomes depressive. Prior to full planing, the excess change of trim to which the warped plane is subjected results first in a reduction of wetted surface. In smooth water the benefits to speed is immediate. The true monohedron, on the other hand, maintains its trim and full wetted surface in this sub-planing range prior to receiving bodily lift.

It would seem that the constant section form with rounded bilges and upward sloping buttock lines, perhaps very slightly hooked just forward of the transom, may be the most efficient medium range performer.

This analysis suggests that the modern hull capable of more than displacement hull speeds should be somewhat modified for designed performance in that range where the last hump in the curve of resistance occurs, namely, at a speed-length ratio of 1.5. Its upward sloping buttock lines, rounded bilges and generally double wedge form will reduce the height of bow and stern waves, result in a maximum of virtual lengthening and mitigate the effect of form on frictional resistance.

The accompanying lines of a 40-footer were developed for a sport fisherman intended for operation at speeds of around 15 knots. In this range, the pure monohedron would be operating below maximum efficiency. Therefore the C.B. was held nearer to midships as in displacement hull practice but the C.F. was moved very close to 60 per cent aft. Buttock lines inboard were given a pronounced slope, only the outboard buttocks retaining parallelism. The result is definitely suggestive of the double wedge form.

Actual performance of the finished boat bears out the fact that much of the planing hull's steadiness, the feeling that the boat is "running on a track," can be retained at sub-planing speeds without the usual sacrifice in speed-power relationship.

In this range of those speeds where planing action is fully developed, the monohedron principle of relatively constant sections, foreshortened planing surface and easy riding entrance finds itself accepted in every part of the

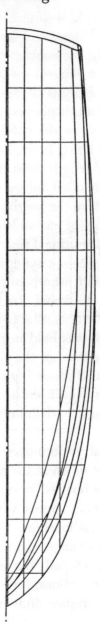

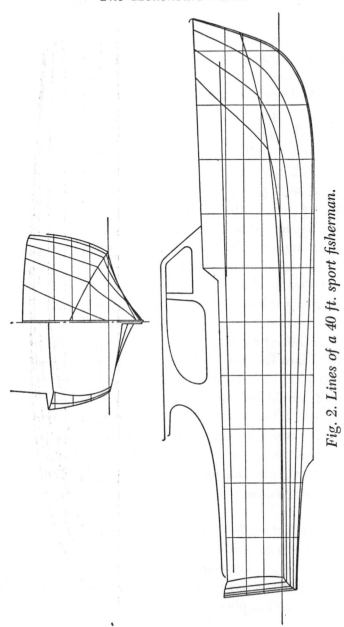

Fig. 2. Lines of a 40 ft. sport fisherman.

world only some five years after its principles were corre-lated and the name itself coined. However, as so fre-quently happens in other fields, its features are being adapted and absorbed into a variety of designs to the benefit of naval architecture as a whole. The monohedron hull as a type has been so rapidly absorbed into general design that most newly developed power craft today are reflecting its influence.

As originally set forth, the pure monohedron principle emphasized parallel buttock lines and relatively short planing surface, that is, a constant section afterbody and wide aspect ratio. These basic features, together with a soft riding spray deflecting entrance still characterize the well designed planing hull. However, today's emphasis has naturally shifted somewhat to various adaptations of monohedron design more suited to the moderate speeds and pocketbooks of post-war owners. By deliberate intent, the monohedron was never a proprietary idea. It was tossed into free competition with the avowed hope that its general use would bring about refinement faster and that it would be more beneficial to the profession.

The first five years seems to indicate the scientific and ethical correctness of both the principle and the proce-dure and to augur well for the necessary further refine-ments as more and more designers apply themselves to the improvement of faster hulls.

Editor's Note: The S/L ratios mentioned in this paper; i.e. in the region of 2 would apply only to what might be called "large small boats." For the average fast pleasure craft the S/L ratios would be higher but the monohedron principle still applies.

Chapter Three

TUNNEL STERNS

By WILLIAM GARDEN

SHALLOW draft power boats are one of the most interesting and poorly understood problems with which the
naval architect is confronted. The design and construction of such a tunnel constitutes a subject which can stand
considerable research. The following notes should be of
value to the practicing designer or student, and, while
the observations are not conclusive in every respect, they
will perhaps help in eliminating the occasional faulty tunnel designs of the past.

Since the majority of the river waterways of the west
are unimproved to a large extent, extreme shallow draft
boats only will be considered. The use of Kort nozzles or
the standard hull forms familiar in the central inland
waterways have been adequately covered and perfected
and since they operate in channels of controlled depth

and are not of extreme shallow draft, the type is outside the realm of this paper.

Over a period of years a designer gradually accumulates a mass of data and reference on almost every subject concerning marine design, propulsion, and marine engineering in general. It is interesting to note that my file on tunnels goes back about forty years, embracing about 250 boats designed for every service by men both familiar and unfamiliar with the type. In this accumulation approximately one-third of the designs are faulty and the resulting boats exhibited such faults as the tunnel breaking water at the transom.

However, the most noteworthy fact is a complete lack of either technical or "rule of thumb" data regarding the subject. The standard works on naval architecture are principally concerned with ship forms and calculations.

Of the boats in the file of my own design I have exact data and, in addition, I have performance data on about a dozen done by other designers in the past few years. Unfortunately, like a lot of information that finds its way into print, a great deal of that published is faulty or misleading, and several unsatisfactory boats have been favorably publicized through gullible reporting. Of those mentioned, all required alteration, from minor acceptable changes, such as rudder balance, to major repairs and reconstruction.

The principal trouble seems centered along steering. Some will steer only while aided by the added directional stability of a barge being pushed ahead, while others lack the rudder power to do much in the way of ship handling or rapid maneuvering.

By following a few basic rules and forms many of these

troubles can be avoided at a great saving in alteration costs after the boat is in service.

The following "rules of thumb" will do to use as a guide:

(1) A safe immersion depth of the screw is about 60 per cent while the boat is at rest.

(2) The tunnel must never clear the surface aft and must be absolutely airtight to avoid cavitation.

(3) The rudder must be designed to avoid choking off the tunnel when hard over.

(4) The merging of the tunnel and bottom must be an easy arc made without a chine or angle, and the bilges must be raised and eased as much as possible to get clear water to the wheel.

(5) In fast tunnel boats the reverse downward hook of the tunnel line in profile must be as easy as possible to avoid elevating the stern through propeller wash on the after sections.

(6) The tunnel hatch should be fitted with substantial wing nuts for rapid removal.

(7) Propeller speed should be kept to the minimum possible. The most efficient wheel speed will result in a pitch ratio of about one.

A few notes might help to clarify the rules. The immersion depth rule is safe. However, propellers will operate in considerable less depth if the tunnel form is properly done. A simple test of possible immersions can be made by gradually lifting a boat in the slings of a small boat yard and observing the reaction at various depths. Don't allow the tunnel to break water, however, or the experiment will be inconclusive.

After the propeller is turning, all of the air is knocked

out of the tunnel causing a head of water to rush up into the vacuum. Through any leak whatsoever, nature will try to relieve the situation with air so every possible opening must be stopped. Although the tunnel is full of water the leaks are air leaks and outward bound so they are difficult to find. One method of spotting them is by going down into the lazarette with a cigar and observing the smoke drifting into any opening. A handful of caulking cotton pulled apart and dropped will also indicate the holes. Wooden tunnels are the chief offenders and should be carefully examined before each season. In one instance during a fast turn, a leaky wooden tunnel lost its prime and the boat ran up on a bar through loss of rudder power due to the wheel pumping air past the rudder. Steel tunnels require less maintenance, but lots of things can happen even here. The easiest mistake to make seems to be to overlook replacing the inspection hatch gasket after examining the propeller.

Steering is the hardest problem of all and probably can be best covered under rule No. 4 pertaining to the chine section. A widely accepted type of western tunnel consists of a scoop out of the bottom with sharp or slightly rounded chines. With a rudder set up in such a tunnel any angle of the rudder blade simply chokes off the tunnel release and creates a lot of turbulence with very little resultant steering action. By easing the sharp chine and running the bilge up as shown in the sketch, the propeller wash has someplace to go. Also this type of stern shown allows proper space for backing rudders if these are fitted.

Another fault of the hard chine tunnel is the trouble many boats have of steering one way and not the other, since, while the wheel is turning, the part of the lower blade visible below the bottom is working in undisturbed water and kicking the stern one way while going ahead and the other while backing down. By easing the chines this trouble is minimized. Some improvement can be made by putting a vane of one-quarter inch plate about 14 or 18 inches wide directly abaft the propeller. We have done this on a couple of boats that didn't steer and the results were worth the effort.

The easy merging of tunnel and bottom cannot be too greatly emphasized. In this type the tunnel chines have been entirely eliminated resulting in an easy sweep from bilge to center line. This type will steer like a normal boat and will steer equally well either to port or starboard while backing down. With the hard chine type it sometimes takes a good guesser to tell which way she will steer even while going ahead. Another fact very seldom considered is that while operating in extremely shallow water the propeller must get a lot of water from the sides as well as underneath due to the proximity of the bottom. By raising the bilges aft, the best results may be obtained.

The profile line and distribution of volume of the tunnel is something that can stand a lot of experimental work. Possibly the prismatic or similar co-efficient of the tunnel itself would do as a basis of compromise or a standard series area curve worked out for various speed length ratios of the tunnel.

Development along this line would involve a very unusual proportion of prismatic co-efficient to speed-length ratios. The downward hook to the profile aft should terminate just below the surface and be as flat as possible to avoid kicking the stern up through action of the pro-

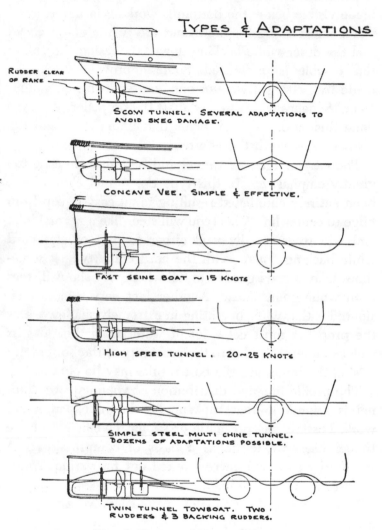

TYPES & ADAPTATIONS

RUDDER CLEAR OF RAKE

SCOW TUNNEL. SEVERAL ADAPTATIONS TO AVOID SKEG DAMAGE.

CONCAVE VEE. SIMPLE & EFFECTIVE.

FAST SEINE BOAT ~ 15 KNOTS

HIGH SPEED TUNNEL. 20~25 KNOTS

SIMPLE STEEL MULTI CHINE TUNNEL. DOZENS OF ADAPTATIONS POSSIBLE.

TWIN TUNNEL TOWBOAT. TWO RUDDERS & 3 BACKING RUDDERS.

Fig. 3. Types of Tunnel Sterns

peller water on the inclined surface. Usually the shaft center line is almost horizontal, which increases the tendency. Many river boats have a tendency to root because of this reaction, so a boat of any speed must have a good lift to the forward sections.

The access hatch to the tunnel should be made of decent size and fitted with quick-acting dogs to hold it in place. A simple hatch will be appreciated when the wheel must be replaced in a hurry or if the boat has been moored bow downstream and the tunnel is filled with drift.

In practice almost any form seems to work from a V to a box with the corners knocked off. Some angularity in profile does not bother the efficiency measurably. Some interesting results can be obtained along this line by a study of flow patterns with a plastic tunnel model and streaks of dye. The attached sketch shows some sections easily fabricated from steel. The steel tunnels seem to work out best in a wooden boat since stern tube, rudder tube strut, and bearings can all be an integral part of the tunnel unit. The problems of alignment or tightness are simplified, damage from gravel and drift is cut down, and work can be done much easier in the welding shop than working overhead in the boat shop.

In conclusion, I should like to point out that no tunnel at all is superior to the best possible tunnel. Tunnel sterns should only be used where there is a draft limitation.

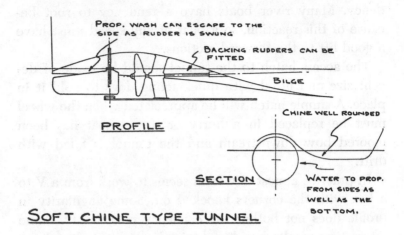

PROP. WASH CAN ESCAPE TO THE
SIDE AS RUDDER IS SWUNG

BACKING RUDDERS CAN BE
FITTED

BILGE

PROFILE

CHINE WELL ROUNDED

SECTION

WATER TO PROP.
FROM SIDES AS
WELL AS THE
BOTTOM.

SOFT CHINE TYPE TUNNEL

RUDDER BLOCKS TUNNEL,
WHEN SWUNG OVER 10°

BILGE

PROFILE

SECTION

TYPICAL FAULTY WESTERN TYPE
CHINES PARALLEL SIMILAR TO A SPLIT PIPE

Fig. 4. Soft Chine and Western Type Tunnels

Chapter Four

THE PLASTIC BOAT, PRO AND CON

By LUTHER H. TARBOX

PLASTIC boats are by no means new. The design and construction of plastic small craft dates from 1876 in this country. A George Waters of Troy, N.Y. started the manufacture of laminated paper rowing shells in that year using shellac as an adhesive bond, combining several layers of paper, bonded with shellac, into a light weight, tough laminate. Using this material he built rowing shells 28 feet overall which weighed, complete, with outriggers and sliding seat, 22 lbs.

One of his paper canoes cruised from Troy, N.Y. to Cedar Keys, Fla., using an "ash breeze" for power, a voyage of some five months duration. During this cruise the canoe suffered no damage other than minor scratches and was found, upon arrival at Cedar Keys, to be in excellent condition. Nathaniel H. Bishop, who made this cruise in a paper canoe, was a hardy man indeed. We do not seem to breed such hardy sailors these days.

A more recent example of these paper laminated plastic boats is Sam Rabl's (a member of the SSCD) design for a very nice kayak, whose plans were published in the very first issue of *How To Build Twenty Boats*. Her construction consisted of a light, strong frame of spruce, employing steam-bent transverse frames, closely spaced, over which closely spaced longitudinal stringers were secured. The skin consisted of three layers of heavy brown wrapping paper, a roll of which was cut crosswise into 3″ wide strips with a saw, and laid diagonally across the frame of the boat, bedded in airplane dope, with a membrane of muslin between each course of paper. The deck was of Flightex airplane cotton, doped to secure and to stretch drum-tight. The result was a light, strong hull having excellent seaworthy qualities and a dream to drive along with double paddles.

The most serious development program in the plastic boat field has been government sponsored. The Navy's BuShips became interested in the fiberglass boat in 1942 when a firm introduced a laminated plastic boat using a thermo-plastic resin dissolved in a volatile solvent as a bonding material. The firm introducing this particular boat apparently hadn't the least idea of the fundamentals of naval architecture and good hull form, for the performance of their boat was so poor that it killed what interest BuShips had in their particular development of the plastic boat. However, in 1945, the design was modified and a fairly large contract for plastic surf boats was issued the company, contract being terminated shortly after VJ Day.

In the past few years BuShips has been very active in the development of the fiberglass boat, placing several different development contracts for this type in 1946 for 28-foot personal boats. The Winner Mfg. Co., Marco Chemical, Inc., The Anchorage, etc. have been instrumental in the development of these particular fiberglass boats.

Modern development of the plastic boat is, for the most part, due to the development of polyester thermosetting resins which bond very well with a fibrous material such as fiberglass cloth and fiberglass mat. Developed early in World War II, these resins were used exclusively for aircraft applications such as glass laminates for self-sealing fuel tanks, etc. Since the war, these polyester groups of resin adhesives have entered the domestic market in plastic and fiberglass laminates wherever high strength and stability of the finished product are required.

Essentially, the fiberglass boat hull consists of a laminate or sandwich consisting of alternate layers of fiberglass cloth and fiberglass mat, each completely saturated with polyester resin which sets up into a homogeneous shell of considerable strength and stability. The laminate is laid up over or into a mold, which is of the form of the boat's hull. There are several methods of procedure employed in setting up this type of hull. One method employs the use of mating male and female molds, wherein the laminates of fiberglass cloth and mat laid over the male mold and the female mold lowered over the raw laminate, all openings sealed with suitable gaskets, supply hoses connected between female mold and resin tank at various locations on the female mold, riser vents attached to female mold, liquid sight glasses attached to female mold to permit visual checking on resin flow and then the valves are opened in resin supply lines allowing the resin to flow into the set-up molds, saturating the fiberglass laminate. This method of resin application, in a fair-sized hull, requires approximately 8 hours to completely saturate the glass laminate and approximately 48 hours are required for curing before the female mold can be lifted off the rough fiberglass hull and hull lifted clear of the male mold.

Another method of set-up consists of a female mold, in which the raw laminate is laid up, each layer coated with resin before the next layer goes in, then a plastic bag, of a form approximating the shape of the inside of finished hull, is placed into the mold over the edges and properly sealed, resin supply tubes placed around the edges of bag, air pressure turned into bag and resin supply valves opened to insure further resin saturation by the laminate which the air pressure within bag insures even pressure application all over the raw laminate.

Both the above methods of set-up are suitable for large scale production only, since mold cost is high and equipment costly as well. It is also questionable if either of the above outlined methods have any advantage, production costwise, over the methods of mold set-up which follow.

The third and perhaps the best method of mold set-up is to use the male mold only, whether one or just a few boats are to be built from the mold. It even can be used to advantage if only one boat is to be built. The number of boats built will determine the amount of time and the cost of mold material which would be used. If a straight-sectioned V-bottomed hull is to be built, the mold can consist of wooden molds, erected on station lines and covered with Masonite or Beaverboard, taking care to allow for both the thickness of the fiberglass laminate and of the Masonite or Beaverboard when lifting the shape of the station molds from the loft drawing. Obviously, the station molds may be constructed of scrap lumber.

Where a shapely V-bottom or round bottom design is to be built, a plaster of paris mold may be used to advantage and is constructed in the following manner: A male buck is built consisting of wooden molds on station lines; molds cut about 2″ scant of the molded lines of the hull, that is 2″ scant of the inside skin of the hull, and fairly closely spaced battens let in flush with the edges are secured to the molds. The battens are then covered with light chicken wire, well-stretched over the battens and molds. This foundation structure of wooden molds and battens, covered with chicken wire, is called a male buck. Over this buck, plaster of paris is troweled on, inserting common burlap in the plaster of paris as a reinforcement. It is necessary to use female templates at each station to insure that the surface of the plaster of paris mold conforms fairly well to the lines of the boat. When thoroughly dry and hard, the surface of the plaster of paris coating can be scraped and sanded to shape as required. Also, it can be grooved as required for longitudinal skin stiffeners and web frames. When finished, the plaster of paris mold should be given a couple of coats of a good wood sealer. It then should be waxed well with Simonize or equal. For a production job, it might be well to consider on all-wood male mold, with regular molds cut to station lines and planked up with say ½″ x 2″ soft wood strips, using the so-called strip-built method, which then can be planed and sanded smooth to the molded lines of the boat. Of course, this all-wood mold must be covered with a good wood sealer.

A female mold of fiberglass laminate can be produced from a male mold such as is described above and does have the advantage that the outside surface of the hull will probably be smoother than would a hull laid up over a male mold, but there is the disadvantage that it is more difficult to lay up the fiberglass cloth and mat into the female and it is much more difficult to determine visually whether there is good saturation of fiberglass cloth and mat with the polyester resin.

Molds have to be thoroughly coated with a parting agent to prevent the fiberglass cloth from bonding to the mold surfaces. Failure to get a complete coverage can lead to very serious trouble.

Of extreme importance, in view of mold costs and the fact that usually many boats will be built over the same mold, is the matter of suitable design for the lines of the fiberglass boat. In the writer's opinion, only the best possible design should be built to in fiberglass, for if the design is not the best possible to devise for the intended service, a lot of very indifferent boats will be produced.

A good example of this is the case of a certain fiberglass dink the Navy is procuring for use as tenders aboard Navy small craft and which are intended for use with a 3 hp outboard motor. The lines of this particular dink would, at best, make a not too good sailing dink, but for the intended use with power, it is about the worst possible dink that could be devised. This example is just another case of the rather stupid methods of government agency procurement regulations which call for requests for bids from at least three vendors and then the one submitting the lowest bid gets the contract; which, while it might be just ducky for buying sealing wax, peanuts or red ink, just doesn't make sense where a boat or an airplane is concerned.

The October 10th, 1952 issue of *Boating Industry* carried a comprehensive article on the production of the Navy's fiberglass (LCVP) landing craft, which explains fully the use of mating male and female molds and the injection system of plasticizing the fiberglass laminate. Charles Bell's fine article in the January and February 1953 issues of *Motor Boating* entitled "Ike Goes Fiberglass" explains the use of the simple beaverboard male mold and describes the building of a fiberglass boat with wood and plywood framing and bulkheads. The January '53 issue of *Road and Track* in an article entitled "How to Build a Fiberglas Body" explains the construction of a male buck, male mold of plaster of paris and a female fiberglass mold, as well as giving sources of materials. All of the above-mentioned articles should be referred to by those desiring complete information on the construction of plastic boats for construction methods and practices are quite well covered.

Very little consideration on the part of designers and builders of the fiberglass boat has been given to the vital subject of adequate hull framing in this type of hull. This lack of engineering forethought on their part is undoubtedly due to the misconception that monocoque, or stressed skin type of construction, requires no framing to support the skin because of shape and being "all in one piece," pointing to aircraft design as example. However, the writer must point out that monocoque construction of aircraft fuselages require framing up with closely spaced longitudinal skin stiffeners and widely spaced transversed webs. This has been true from the very earliest examples of monocoque fuselage construction in aircraft as can be seen in the old Albatross D 3 to 5 A, Rumpler D 3, Junkers D 1 to D 3; all World War I fighter planes, up to the present day jets. As a rule of thumb, it can be stated that the supporting framing for stressed skin of monocoque construction, whether of molded plywood, aluminum alloy, welded steel, or molded fiberglass, must be such that the maximum deflection of the skin between supports must not exceed 1/360th of the span, unsupported, that is. And, by the way, this applies more or less to any boat's hull unless that type of construction be very flexible, such as, for example, a clinker-built hull. It must be kept in mind at all times that modern synthetic resins of the urea, resorcinol and polyester groups are not too flexible and do not take continuous flexure without failure. The large deflections often noticed in molded plywood hulls may well be the reason why many of these molded boats have such a relatively short life in fairly rough service and also why many of the stock plywood outboards and kit boats go to pieces in a comparatively few seasons of use.

Adequate framing of any of the molded or stressed skin boats calls for considerable stress analysis on the part of the designer. Investigation of the dynamic bending moments (hogging and sagging) can be approximated and section modulus of the hull structure calculated as required. So also may transverse web frames and longitudinal skin stiffeners with sufficient accuracy to suit the needs of the design. The student and young designer should refer to Lindsay Lord's *Naval Architecture of Planing Hulls*, Kent's *Mechanical Engineer's Handbook*, Roussel and Chapman's *Principles of Naval Architecture*, etc. for the required information on the simple stress analysis required.

As previously mentioned, the skin of the molded fiberglass boats consists of a laminate of fiberglass cloth and fiberglass mat, laid over or into a suitable mold in alternate layers, then bonded together with a suitable thermosetting polyester resin adhesive. As a rule of thumb, a 12-foot dinghy's fiberglass skin can consist of three layers of fiberglass boat cloth and two layers of fiberglass mat, an 18-foot or 20-foot boat can have a laminate consisting of three layers of cloth and two of mat in the topsides and four layers of cloth and three of mat in the bottom. Fuel or water tanks can be laid up of two layers of cloth and one of mat. Such a fuel or water tank may possibly outlast light gauge galvanized steel tanks by quite a few years, if the tanks used on some of the World War II aircraft rescue boats are any criteria.

The material used for framing the molded fiberglass boat calls for considerable thought on the part of the designer. Use of wood, plywood, aluminum alloy, or other metal framing is poor practice since the coefficient of linear expansion of such framing differs considerably from that of the fiberglass laminate and, in consequence, either the laminate or the framing will be eventually in the region of contact.

An example: A certain fiberglass dinghy, built a few years back, had longitudinal mahogany stiffeners placed

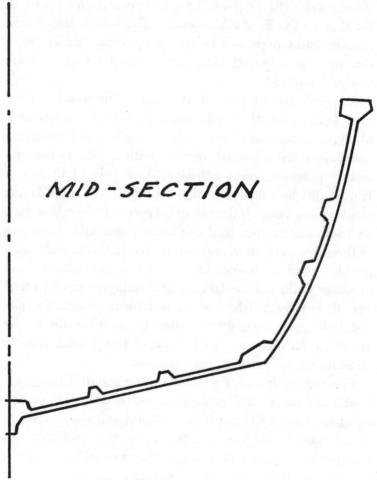

Fig. 5. Mid-section of a plastic boat

just below the inner layer of fiberglass cloth in way of the bottom skin. In two years, moisture had seeped through the fiberglass cloth, causing the wood to swell or expand with sufficient force as to split the fiberglass cloth and the mahogany rotted out, leaving a very weakened bottom skin in the boat. It is the writer's opinion that framing for the fiberglass boat must also be of fiberglass if reasonable service life is desired.

It would not be difficult to build up frames and stiffeners for a fiberglass hull using the basic fiberglass material in the form of glass strands, called "roving strands" in the trade, properly impregnating the strands with polyester resin, shaping to the size desired, and covering with two layers of fiberglass strip, bonded, of course, to the strands, to each other and to the inside of the fiberglass skin with polyester resin. The illustrations show the suggested type of fiberglass framing believed most suitable for these molded "glass" boats. Note that the inner strip of fiberglass is narrower than the outer, permitting a greater bonding area in shear at the attachment to the hull's skin. The fact that the bond used in the fiberglass boat is strong in shear and weak in direct tension would be kept in mind when designing framing for this type of boat.

Such fiberglass framing will have the same coefficient of linear expansion as the skin or laminate and there will therefore be no thermal or swelling-shrinking stresses other than slight stresses which might result from unequal heating of skin and frames due to unequal exposure to the sun's rays. The advantages of frames built up of fiberglass is obvious in view of the above.

Considerable attention should also be given to design details, especially those relating to the attachments of

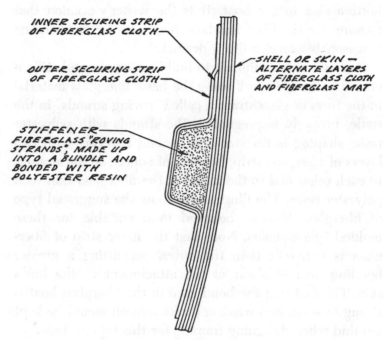

INNER SECURING STRIP
OF FIBERGLASS CLOTH

OUTER SECURING STRIP
OF FIBERGLASS CLOTH

SHELL OR SKIN —
ALTERNATE LAYERS
OF FIBERGLASS CLOTH
AND FIBERGLASS MAT

STIFFENER
FIBERGLASS "ROVING
STRANDS", MADE UP
INTO A BUNDLE AND
BONDED WITH
POLYESTER RESIN

Fig. 6. Suggested construction of fiberglass stiffener.

fittings subject to any appreciable amount of stress or strain. If just secured with through-bolts with nuts set up over washers, or by means of studs in the threaded holes or self-tapping screws, vibration and working of the hull causes enough chafing of the laminate so that the fastening hole gradually enlarges, loosening the fastening. Prevention of this evil condition consists of small insert plates of aluminum alloy or other metal, imbedded in the laminate; the insert plate having numerous ½″ holes equally spaced clear of the fastening holes which allow the fiberglass on each side of insert plate to be bonded together at regular intervals in way of the insert plate.

Very small craft, such as small dinghies, might well be of pure monocoque construction if built of fiberglass laminate, with longitudinal stiffening only at keel or gunwales, but only if they are rowing or sailing dinghies designed for high performance with outboard or inboard power require additional framing. Larger craft will require framing as previously mentioned.

Panel breakers, in the form of longitudinal stiffeners and fairly widely spaced web frames in conjunction with or without bulkheads are required to prevent panting of the fiberglass laminate skin and its resultant easy destruction.

The sagging moment due to the hull pitching in a sea in fairly high speeds should be checked. This is not difficult nor does the calculation consume much time. So that SSCD members will have available a reference where this type of loading calculation can be previewed in greater detail, the example given in Lindsay Lord's book has been followed.

Tensile strength for fiberglass is claimed to run as high

as 300,000 lbs/in. However, in a fiberglass laminate used as boat plank skin, only part of the fiberglass fibers run longitudinally, and it is these longitudinal fibers which resist bending. In a fiberglass laminate consisting of 40% fiberglass, perhaps not more than 10% of the total fibers run longitudinally, for, remember in a laminate, a five-course laminate consists of three layers of mat and in the mat the fibers are so crisscrossed that none of the mat can be considered as running longitudinally. Thus our ultimate tensile for such a laminate drops to 30,000 lbs/in.

There is another indeterminate which further reduces the ultimate value for tensile strength. The fact that there is always some uncertainty in the strength of the cured resin, the possibility that there might be some air bubbles entrained in the laminate plus the fact that the cured resin bond is weak in direct tension is sufficient reason to reduce the value of the safe tensile for a fiberglass laminate to 1/10th of the ultimate, or 3,000 lbs/in. in the writer's opinion.

For design purposes, the unit weight of 40% fiberglass laminate can be taken as 107 pounds per cu. ft. While there will be a minimum amount of fastenings to consider, since fastenings are needed only to secure fittings to the hull, weights of metal foundation inserts used in securing fittings to the hull must be considered and carefully calculated. One other item for the weight calculation which must be considered is paint; it is probably that 3 coats of paint over a fiberglass laminate will approximate 0.23 pounds per square foot.

It is the writer's opinion that the use of dyes mixed into the polyester resins used to bond fiberglass laminate boat hulls is a mistake, quite aside from the fact that such incorporated dyes hardly ever give a smooth, even coat of color. The fiberglass laminate, while water resistant, is not wholly watertight in itself—it can and does soak water. It can be waterproofed with paint coatings and therefore it should be painted. The bare, unfinished hull surfaces should be given a coat of a good wood sealer, then two or three coats of color. Further, there is another good reason for avoiding the use of dyes mixed into the polyester resin—there is a possibility that such dyes weaken the cured resin bond and this is logical for a dye certainly cannot add to the bonding ability of the cured resin and being a sort of extender, it must, to some extent, reduce the strength of the liquid resin somewhat, like a bootlegger cutting good corn liquor. Since the surface of the fiberglass laminate can be smoothed up so nicely with an electric sander, a paint finish can be smooth and "yachty"—another good reason for painting.

In its present state of development, the plastic fiberglass boat can be considered experimental only so far as the use of the material is concerned. Only time will tell whether the material is durable and satisfactory to a degree where it will equal wood or welded steel or fabricated aluminum alloy for a boat building material. Five years from now, or ten years, will give us a better idea on just how good this material is for boats.

On the standpoint of cost, the material appears quite favorable, since while the cost of lumber and metals tend to increase, fiberglass materials costs seem to trend lower. Simple, low-cost molds would have to be used if the cost be comparable and but one or just a few boats are to be built to design.

There is the drawback that trained labor on this material will be hard to come by for a long time to come and considerable on-the-job training on the part of the boatbuilder will be very necessary before the shop can be expected to turn out a top quality job.

It therefore behooves the designer wishing to work with this material to learn all he can of it, for it is the designer who will have to impart a working knowledge of plastic fiberglass construction to the builder in a good many instances. It also follows that the designer must supervise the construction with care in order that a reasonably good boat be the result of the builder's efforts.

It is of the utmost importance that the design of the fiberglass boat be given the most careful consideration by the designer, errors in design judgment, just plain carelessness or impractical ideas can be ruinous to the orderly development of this type. The use of large doses of horse sense is indicated, otherwise, the orderly, progressive development of the plastic fiberglass boat is unlikely.

A word of warning: fiberglass boats, being heavier than water, will sink if swamped unless there are built-in flotation tanks. The young designer must always keep this important fact in mind when working with the material.

The use of fiberglass laminates as a boatbuilding material seems to offer the following good and bad points:

1. Finished hull may be light in weight.
2. High unit strength/weight ratio.
3. Resistant to bending stresses, shear and impact. Note that the material has been used as a form of plastic armor in bulletproof vests, armor for light motor vehicles, ships and planes.
4. Can be molded into any desired shape with the ex-

ception of sharp corners. Some fillet or corner radius must be tolerated.

5. One piece hull construction is obtainable.
6. Very small craft can be pure monocoque.
7. Properly painted, the hull is watertight.
8. Appears to have low maintenance costs, provided the material proves to be durable.
9. Costs appear to be improving favorably.
10. Very smooth hull surfaces are obtainable.
11. Lends itself readily to mass production.
12. Not subject to dry rot, corrosion or teredo attacks.

Disadvantages might be listed as:

1. Durability unproven.
2. Requires careful supervisory control to insure complete saturating of the fiberglass laminate with the polyester resin.
3. Supervisory force must possess a thorough knowledge of the characteristics and limitations of the material.
4. Design requires extreme care on the designer's part.
5. Requires thorough plan detailing, therefore design costs will be on the high side.
6. Bonding is weak in direction of tension.
7. Attachments to hull structure by means of screws, pivots, bolts, etc. likely to chafe loose if not reinforced with perforated metal insert plates encased in the fiberglass laminate.
8. Practically impossible to have nicely finished brightwork in the traditional yacht fashion.

Model hulls of fiberglass laminates do hold considerable promise. The designer can easily produce a series of models for test purposes by a series of slight alterations to the male mold used to lay up the fiberglass model, thus could obtain interesting and valuable trial results. Use of a plaster of paris male mold would be ideal since the mold surface is easily shaped with sharp hand tools.

Powered model trials would be possible, using a model airplane gas engine for power, the performance of engine can be checked with a vibratak. If the same engine and propeller were used to power a model series and model test runs made in a smooth water pond, models tethered to a pylon in the center and the same tether used, having a convenient length for converting to ft/sec or ft/min or mph, and time around checked with a stop watch, some very interesting and informative results might be obtained. The designer would further benefit from the use of fiberglass models in that he would gain considerable experience in using the material.

Chapter Five

THE SMALL CRAFT DESIGNER AND THE COMMERCIAL BOAT

By ROBERT F. SCHNEIDER

THIS monograph deals with a portion of the field of vessel design rather than with a technical problem or with the design of a particular craft.

The taxational hijacking of upper bracket incomes has nearly eliminated yachting in large vessels; and the big boats are all but gone. They will not be replaced.

The boat designer must therefore confine his work to the smaller pleasure boats, live by some other means or enter upon the middle ground of the commercial boat.

The commercial boat is a vessel designed, constructed, and operated for the purpose of making money. Keep that in mind—it is fundamental. For the purposes of this paper, the upper limit of size is set to include tugs, most fishing craft, coastwise tankers, and the smaller ferries— for they are about the largest craft the design of which can be, save in a cursory way, the work of one person.

For the benefit of those who delight in the competitive activities of the hydroplane, ocean racer, or class sailboat, and who may feel that the working boat is less glamorous, let it be remembered that the commercial craft is racing all the time. To fulfill the primary requisite of making a profit it races continuously against time and money. It races against time to dock or undock the greatest number of steamships in a given period, to shift more barges per day, to catch more fish and be first to market, to deliver more fuel oil per load and yet pump out and be gone without awaiting the next tide. And at the same time a financial race is going on, in which the income from the vessel's operations races against the costs of interest, depreciation, insurance, upkeep, repairs, fuel and stores, and payroll. The third race is against lost time. Availability is a major factor; and losses of working time for upkeep, periodic overhaul, and damage repairs must be both infrequent and brief. A tug which is not at work does its resting to the tune of around $600.00 a day, a coastwise tanker around $800.00 or $900.00.

The best boat for the job is the one which, under the conditions at hand, makes the best combined score for the three simultaneous events. It must do the most work, for the least money, with the fewest and briefest interruptions.

Surely, in such a field, the new designer with small craft background will find problems that are of absorbing interest and whose challenges are worthy of his skill.

The entrance into the field of the commercial boat is, in the opinion of the writer, logically by way of small craft design. Much like the situation prevalent in approaching the designs of yachts, pre-existing, accurate data, from sources other than the designer's own notes, on performance of similar craft or craft in similar usage is not readily available, at least in complete form. There is seldom the time or money for elaborate preliminary experiment—such as tank tests.

Features of design and construction must be adjusted to the facilities of the building yard. For instance, a series of steel tug hulls of multiple chine design was developed for construction in a yard which had only a very small plate furnace and no loftsman capable of developing shell plate.

Scantlings are more often determined, as in yacht construction, by appraising effects of rough operation, year-on-year wear and tear, weathering, simplified material inventory, and fabrication problems; than from the somewhat formalized calculations for ultimate strength which regulate large hull matters.

Hull forms and coefficients vary widely, as in pleasure boats. Commercial boats which are regarded as nearly alike may vary in their hull forms, coefficients and curve sheets, far more than do large ships which are considered very unlike.

Arrangements, machinery, and equipment span the wide ranges which the small boat designer takes in stride. The deck arrangements and fittings of a fisherman, a tug, or of some other classes of working craft require the observation, understanding, and detailed study necessary for those of the most highly developed racing yacht. Not only must they be convenient, effective, efficient, and as safe as possible; but they must also make their good showing in all weathers, all seasons, daylight, and darkness. Rapid, unimpeded access about and through the boat is as necessary for convenience, safe operation, and efficient working of the commercial boat as it is for any racing craft.

In a number of coastwise tankers built six or seven years ago, the main engine control stand was located so that the pull bells could be heard and the controls most quickly reached—from the galley and the head. Another vessel, very similar, but not so conveniently arranged in this respect, was required to carry larger engine room crew.

As in yachting, appearance counts. A working boat, designed with reasonable regard to matters of appearance, not only appeals to the prospective owner and increases future resale value, but also acts as a favorable, and often very important, piece of company publicity wherever it goes.

There are at the same time certain outstanding differences between the small pleasure craft and the commercial boat; and recognition of the differences, and at least some study thereof, is of value to any small craft designer, whether he plans to do commercial boat designing or to acquire his troubles elsewhere.

Most obvious of the differences is the established position of steel construction in the commercial vessel field. This has within a few years come to mean welded steel construction. With the exceptions of "crack stoppers" in very large vessels and cold riveting of light material in metal lifeboats, riveting has disappeared from the scene of new construction. In fact, most of the repairs to existing riveted hulls are performed by welding. Yet the first successful all welded steel tanker was built in 1928, and the first two all welded steel tugs in 1934—so rapidly has the change occurred. The tanker and at least one of the tugs are still in active operation. Today the designer of commercial boats must know both wooden and welded steel construction.

But, in the opinion of the writer, the greatest fundamental difference is that of operating time. The operating time for the power plant of a fairly active pleasure boat in the vicinity of New York is probably not over 200 hours per year. The main engine of a fairly active tug or tanker often logs 500 to 600 hours per month. A composite fleet average runs 4,000 to 5,000 hours per vessel per year. Overhaul schedules are currently at 8,000 operating hours for main engines and 1,500 for auxiliary high speed engines. Operation is not at "cruising speed" but "hooked up" practically all the time. Consider, for a moment, the power plant of an average pleasure cruiser—after 40 seasons of active operation—run "wide open" at practically all times except when maneuvering—and run all this time with only minor maintenance and routine lubrication!

This, then, calls for some drastic revisions of thinking on the part of the pleasure craft designer in regard to propulsion machinery performance. The nature and extent thereof is not within the scope of this paper, other than to say that loss of operating time because of machinery upkeep and repairing must be minimized.

The operation of various types of fishing gear must be understood if the designer is to do work in the fishing fleets. Such knowledge must usually be gained locally since operating conditions and practices vary widely according to locality and change almost from year to year. Here indeed is a field for experiment and development.

Many features of present operating practices leave room for important improvements; and the designer who can solve some of the problems will find himself in demand.

For example, the oystering industry has been experimenting with various methods of stocking, dredging, and clearing of cultivated beds. Thus far, the experiments have not been on a large scale, although several novel vessels have been put into operation, with varying and hotly debated results. The pressure of increasing costs of present methods, both in labor and damaged stock, is attracting interest and money to the improvement of methods, vessels, and gear. Here is a definite set of problems and an open opportunity. It is but one of many.

Expansion of the chemical industries has made bulk water transportation of chemicals a fact. Both barges and self-propelled craft are used. The field is just opening. It is economically sound; and cargo volume and diversity seem almost without limit.

Water transportation of solid and liquid fuel is probably the largest single section of coastwise and inland water transportation, elsewhere than on the Great Lakes. The economic advantages of bulk oil storage and distribution plants, so sized and located that they must be supplied by vessels of moderate size, assures a steady and still expanding volume of business for motor tankers and tank barges.

Waterside location of bulk fuel terminals, chemical plants, grain elevators, and even larger piers and warehouses, has increased the need for, and interest in, fireboats. The need and demand will probably continue. These vessels present interesting design problems of a highly specialized kind.

While definite figures are, so far as the writer has been able to discover, not available—it appears that, by a great margin, most of the best in commercial boats is the work of individual designers or small design offices and of the smaller yards. Here the individual is not completely submerged. The diversity of the work and problems encountered make the commercial boat a natural field for the small craft designer who, by his training and experience, is accustomed to regard the vessel in its entirety —yet to cope in detail with the diversified phases of its design and construction.

Chapter Six

A METHOD OF DETERMINING CENTERS OF BUOYANCY

By ROBERT F. SCHNEIDER

HULL calculations for loading and stability divide into these steps: determination of weights and their locations; determination of displacements and centers of buoyancy for various conditions of flotation; and calculations of metacentric height, righting arm, etc., from data assembled in the two preceding steps. This paper deals with the second step—determination of displacements and centers of buoyancy.

At first, this may seem to be a somewhat elementary topic. However, it is the writer's observation that the customary procedures of calculation embody certain inherent shortcomings which become increasingly serious as the calculations are extended over widening ranges of loading, trim, and transverse inclination—as would occur when investigating the characteristics of a vessel subject to variable loading.

The writer's conflict with the standard procedure has been the cause of some investigation of the possibilities of improvement; and a somewhat unconventional method of calculation has been evolved. The steps are founded upon established facts of vessel geometry; it is the application of them which is something of a departure. It is proposed to introduce the method first and make comparisons afterward.

Prepare the necessary working sheets, which consist of a body plan, a grid for Bonjean and area curves, and two grids for displacement curves. It is suggested that the working sheets be drawn on tracing material and that the actual work be performed on white background prints of the originals; since, in an extensive investigation, it is convenient to use several prints of each working sheet. Include on each tracing a horizontal and a vertical scale as well as a figure of exactly ten square inches area. By working with the scales as they appear on the print being used and by checking the planimeter on the standard area as it appears on the same print, compensation for print distortion and instrument behavior is simplified.

The body plan is to be drawn as a full body plan—that is, both sides of the vessel are drawn in so that each section is shown in its entirety. Include the line of the deck crown and indicate the baseline and centerline clearly. The sections may be drawn to station lines, frame lines, bulkheads, tank ends, or any combination desired, for it is essential only that the sections be perpendicular to the baseline, square to the centerline, and of such number and location that they accurately delineate the form of the vessel. There is no need to space the sections at speci-

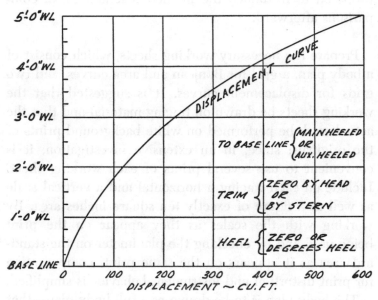

Fig. 7. Arrangement of displacement: Grid 1

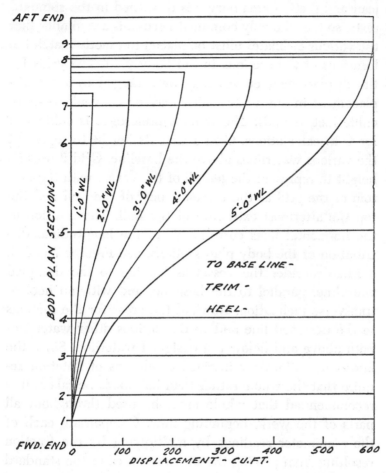

Fig. 8. Arrangement of displacement: Grid 2

fied or uniform intervals; so they may be scattered to suit one's convenience. The preparation of the grid for Bonjean and section area curves is described in the standard texts; so that the only comment needed is a reminder that the various ordinates must be placed to exactly match the locations of the sections in the body plan. The grids for the displacement curves may be arranged to show displacement in any units which may be convenient—tons, cubic feet, pounds. The writer's preference is cubic feet for C.B. calculations. Grid 1 uses its height to represent the various waterlines above the baseline. Grid 2 uses its height to represent the length of the vessel, with the bottom of the grid as the foremost part of the hull and the top the aftermost extremity of the hull. The position of the horizontal lines corresponds to the longitudinal distribution of the body plan sections. See Figures 7 and 8.

First consider the vessel as floating to the designed waterline, parallel to the baseline, and with no heel or transverse inclination. Run out the areas for the sections to the designed line and to the various other waterlines both above and below the designed waterline. Since the later calculations for inclined conditions of flotation require that the whole rather than half areas be taken, it is recommended that whole areas be used throughout all parts of the work, beginning now. Compensate each of the planimeter readings by multiplying by the fraction resulting from placing the measured area of the standard area figure on the same body plan print over the area of the figure as originally drawn. Multiply by the appropriate factor for scale; and with the series of corrected readings construct the Bonjean curves for the conditions of zero trim and zero heel. When setting out the points of the curves, scale the points from the prints of the scales as they appear on the print of the Bonjean and area curve sheet being used. Using the Bonjean curves, construct on the same sheet the area curves of the vessel up to the various waterlines in accordance with the customary procedure. Notice that the endings of the curves for the various waterlines occur at the fore and aft locations of the mold line or fairbody line (steel or wood) for the particular waterline for which the curve is constructed. Especially if there is much overhang or undercut to the profile of the vessel, the area curve endings will spot in at irregular and apparently inconvenient places. Do not be concerned about this.

The displacement volume of the vessel up to the various waterlines may now be calculated by running out with the planimeter the area enclosed by the baseline and the area curve for the waterline being investigated. The area obtained is multiplied by the fraction consisting of the measured area of the standard figure on the sheet being worked over the area of the figure as originally drawn (just as was done with the body plan areas.) Multiply the result by the reciprocal of the product of the vertical and horizontal scales used in drawing the curve. The result is the cubic volume of displacement up to the waterline selected. Repeat the procedure for each area curve. From the series of displacements found, construct the displacement curve on Grid 1 for the existing conditions of zero trim and zero heel. Pause, at this point, to observe that the variations of waterline lengths resulting from overhangs and undercut caused no interference, complication, or inaccuracy.

Now imagine that the vessel is cut off at the lowest

waterline, so that only that portion remains which is above the baseline, but below the lowest waterline. Next imagine that this remaining portion is immersed endwise bow first, as one would lower a sounding rod into a tank. Calculate, using the planimeter, a displacement curve for this imaginary situation. The bottom of the curve will be the point where immersion begins; and the top will be the point at which immersion is complete. Draw in this curve on Grid 2. Now suppose that this time the vessel is cut off not at the lowest waterline, but at the next waterline above, so that now the vessel exists from the baseline up to the second waterline. Repeat the displacement curve calculation and draw in the curve as before. Continue for all waterlines. The calculation is made by measuring the area on the appropriate area curve from the bow to the first body plan section line, then from the bow back to the second line, and so on for the entire length of the area curve. Thus there will be a displacement curve on Grid 2 for each area curve on the Bonjean and area curve sheet. Note that the extremities of the curves, because of overhang and undercut, each probably fall at a different posi-´ tion from that for each other curve. It will presently be seen that here again this does not complicate matters.

So far we have no answers.

Let us digress. Consider Figure 9. AB is the displacement curve of a volume, such as the immersed portion of the hull of a vessel. CD is any vertical line intersecting AB at some point E. FG is any horizontal line intersecting CD at a point H which must be above E and intersecting AB at some point J.

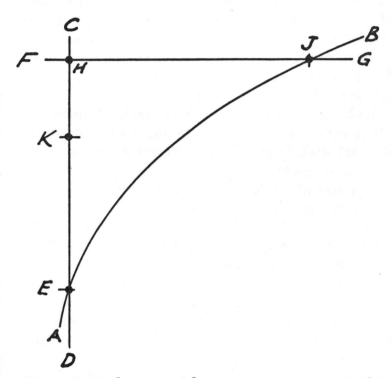

Fig. 9. Vertical center of buoyancy curve, using Grid 1.

The enclosed area EHJ has the interesting and convenient property that, if HK lying along CD and extending downward from H represents the quotient obtained by dividing the enclosed area EHJ by the length HJ, the position of point K is at the vertical location of the center of gravity of that portion of the original volume represented by that portion of the displacement curve AB extending from E to J. Therefore, if the volume represented by EJ is the immersed portion of a vessel, K is the vertical location of its center of buoyancy.

With the previous paragraph in mind, return to displacement curve Grid 1 and note that the various waterlines act similarly to line FG in Figure 9. The left hand edge of the grid corresponds to portion EJ of curve AB. Thus a separate enclosed area is created to represent the conditions up to each waterline marked on the grid. The calculation for the vertical center of buoyancy for displacement up to each waterline therefore follows the procedure just outlined for Figure 9.

Turning now to the series of displacement curves on the print of Grid 2, the center of buoyancy for each is again arrived at by the same process. In these latter cases, it will be seen that, since the curves and grid are all constructed endwise, the centers found are, in relation to the vessel, actually longitudinal centers. Hence, the centers of buoyancy have now been determined vertically and longitudinally for a range of displacements wherein the vessel is at zero longitudinal trim and zero transverse heel. Since the conditions of flotation are all at zero transverse heel, all C.B.'s are on centerline. The C.B. locations for intermediate displacements are along the curve determined by the positions of the calculated points; and their positions may be readily found by interpolation.

The next situation is that involving longitudinal trim. Run in the trimmed waterlines on a new print of the Bonjean and area sheet; transfer the Bonjean curves already calculated; and rework the area curves. Carry through the remainder of the procedure the same as was done for the conditions of zero trim. This latter set of calculations may be repeated for each of whatever number of trims it is desired to investigate; and again values for intermediate conditions may be found by interpolating the curves through the calculated points.

In the investigation of the C.B. positions for conditions not involving transverse heel, it was necessary to fix the locations in only two directions, vertically and longitudinally, since, by reason of the side-for-side symmetry of the conventional vessel form, the C.B.'s for conditions of zero transverse heel are on centerline. However, when heeled conditions are investigated, the points are fixed by one longitudinal calculation, but two transverse ones are required.

Let us now consider the investigation of C.B. locations for conditions involving transverse heel.

Begin, on a print of the body plan, by setting up a heeled baseline AB located at an angle to the normal baseline which is equal to the angle of heeled condition to be investigated, and at such a location that it is entirely outside of, but close to, the body plan. Add any suitable number of heeled waterlines CD-EF-GH etc., parallel to AB. See Figure 10.

On a Bonjean and area curve print, using the baseline

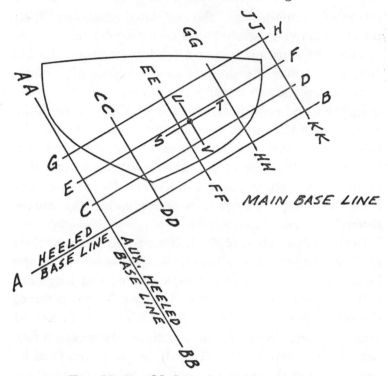

Fig. 10. Establishing heeled waterlines.

for the heeled baseline AB, draw in the heeled waterline CD-EF etc., properly spaced from the baseline and clearly identified. If desired, a heeled profile may be added; but this is not necessary.

Go through the procedures followed for finding the longitudinal C.B. the same as for a vessel in upright position. Prints of the same displacement Grid 2 are used. Thus, the longitudinal C.B.'s are fixed.

Next calculate the vertical C.B.'s in relation to heeled baseline AB in Figure 10. Since the vessel is no longer immersed symmetrically side-for-side, it follows that the C.B.'s are no longer on centerline, but located along lines parallel to the heeled baseline and at the calculated distances above it—for instance, in Figure 10, along line ST for flotation to heeled waterline GH.

Return to the body plan print and set an auxiliary heeled baseline just below and outside the body plan and at right angles to the heeled baseline; and also set up auxiliary heeled waterlines CC-DD, EE-FF, etc. parallel to the auxiliary heeled baseline AA-BB.

Make up a series of displacement curves—first for that part of the body plan only that is located between the heeled baseline AB and the heeled waterline CD—then for that part between AB and EF, and so on. Find the C.B. lines for each displacement. At the crossing of the two lines representing C.B. positions for the same displacement volume—such as W for lines ST and UV, which are both for displacement up to heeled waterline GH—is the heeled vertical and transverse C.B. for that condition of flotation. Since this latter calculation is made to an auxiliary baseline placed at right angles to the waterlines on which the vessel is assumed to be floating, the resultant C.B.'s are actually transverse C.B.'s in relation to the vessel's flotation.

All of these same calculations may also be made for combined conditions of flotation, involving both longitudinal trim and transverse heel.

Once the desired number of points are determined, curves may be constructed to determine intermediate points.

The points and curves determined in all of the preceding calculations may be variously combined into such graphical representations of displacement, heel, trim, and C.B. as may be suited to the problems in hand.

The writer has found that the method of determining C.B.'s here presented has several important advantages. It is highly accurate.

No allowances or auxiliary calculations are required to evaluate the effects of overhang and undercut, since they are taken into full account without recourse to additional steps.

There are no involved mathematical procedures. Arithmetic and a planimeter are all that is needed.

Since much of the work is graphical, errors are easily spotted and readily corrected.

But the point which makes all of these features of practical value is that this method saves time. The greater the range of the calculation, especially in its investigation of conditions involving transverse inclination, the greater the economy of time, both absolute and percentagewise.

Chapter Seven

THE VALUE OF DIMENSIONAL AND NON-DIMENSIONAL CURVES IN PRELIMINARY DESIGN

By THOMAS E. COLVIN

IN dealing with mechanical elements, all necessary units may be derived from three primary units—L, T, and M. Therefore, we may consider that the actual design of a vessel is a dimensional equation—L equaling the length or size and type of vessel, T the time required to design the vessel, and M, the mass of detail required.

Needless to say, in solving for this equation, the end result should equal a profit for the designer. If this is an accepted axiom, then it is essential that each designer turn out work of the highest quality for a reasonable amount of money from the standpoint of each client. It is obvious that there is still a certain amount of detail that must be shown, and a certain number of calculations that must be made prior to the completion of any competent design.

Since calculations and detailing vary directly and more or less in proportion to the type of vessel being designed, it is practically impossible to reduce the amount of time or labor necessary in these two phases of design, even with standardized detail plans, unless the designer has established a rapid method of pre-determining the majority of characteristics and details involved in the new design during the preliminary design stages. By doing so, he eliminates unnecessary redrawing and adjusting of both hull lines and arrangements, and eliminates the possibility of having to re-do his calculations either wholly or partially.

There are many and various systems of speeding up preliminary design which range from modifying an old standby plan to complete lines and arrangement plans, as well as all necessary calculations, redrawing and readjusting them after complete study into the vessel in its final form. The former is rather slipshod and the latter is entirely out of place in the small design office.

Between these two extremes, there lie several methods of estimating the ability and characteristics of a new design. These methods may be divided into two systems —the dimensional, and the non-dimensional analysis of hull forms. Before we continue further, it may be well to redefine the usage of dimensional and non-dimensional characteristics.

Dimensional Comparison

Dimensional pertains to any known or assumed quantity such as length, breadth, depth, cube, etc., or any combined function thereof.

Dimensional comparison is a direct comparison of the similarities of two or more vessels.

Dimensional curves are curves in which a known quantity is plotted on a given ordinate from a given base, such as the curves of form. The primary reason for dimensional curves is to enable one to read desired intermediate values between calculated points. Most dimensional curves may be reduced to non-dimensional by substituting unity for maximum section and all others as functions of unity.

Hulls are enlarged or reduced to a given number of feet and dimensions compared directly. One hundred feet is usually the common length to compare one hull to another. For accurate results with this method, similarity of type is absolutely necessary. The results are more often than not very distorted and of limited value, and it is necessary for the designer to make too many assumptions. "Fudge factors" do not allow an honest direct evaluation and it soon becomes evident that exceptions are more numerous than the rule.

The 10% rule is used quite often, wherein any hull may be enlarged or reduced by 10%. A designer and more often a builder will utilize this method to obtain several stock models using the same molds, but increasing or decreasing either the spacing of the molds or adding or reducing the entire amount of change amidships. The comparisons are much better than those expanded or reduced to 100 feet; however, a greater number of bases are required and fringe distortion is a frequent occurrence. It is then possible to have two conflicting curves serving a given design. It has a limited value when radical departures in hull form or arrangement are made and, as with the 100 foot comparison, "fudge factors" and exceptions are necessary. In both of these comparative analyses, the design is very limited and ratios of beam to draft, length to depth, and

$$\left(\overline{\frac{L}{100}}\right)^3$$

are especially important. When hulls are very similar or almost identical, Froude's law of comparison may be used, which requires identical hull forms. A four-foot model of a 100-foot hull will behave in a similar manner to the actual hull. A model of one vessel will behave in similar ways to another vessel only to a degree of existing similarity. The law of comparison does not imply that a good 60-footer will make a good 30- or 100-footer. Seaworthiness of any design is not an inherent factor, but a designed factor.

Non-Dimensional Comparison

Non-dimensional pertains to any function of shape which is not dependent on or necessarily varies with any linear dimension or any dimensional ratio.

Non-dimensional comparison is the establishment of coefficients which indicate the amount of, or distribution of, mass.

Non-dimensional curves are curves on which the base, L, is any convenient length, and upon which there are ordinates erected at regular or irregular intervals which will be a known percentage of base, L. The length of each ordinate will be in a percentage of the maximum ordinate, which is unity. Non-dimensional curves may become dimensional when a function of a known or desired quantity is substituted for unity.

Similarity of type in non-dimensional comparison is desirable but not necessary. The results are relatively free of any distortion. Of course, the most obvious fact remains that the curves devised as an aid by a designer for his own use will be of less value to another designer unless they happen to think in similar ways. For, given a particular design criteria, each will visualize a hull which has similar characteristics in appearance and shape as other designs of his creation. This method also allows the greatest of freedom to the designer, for, once having established in a sketch the length, profile, shape of the midship section, draft, and tentative arrangement, which is customarily done in the preliminary sketch, it is but a matter of a few hours before an accurate determination of displacement, waterline shape, B.M., deck shape, center of buoyancy, scantlings, weight of bare hull, wetted surface, prismatic coefficient, and sectional area at any given point in the hull may be determined. It is also possible at this stage for a designer to alter, and at times drastically, many aspects of the design and at once determine the effect upon the design. In utilizing this method to its fullest, the designer avails himself of the opportunity to explore a great many ideas and to evaluate them directly without having to draw complete lines plans or arrangements plans. A conservative estimate of time saved would be six hours for yachts, and from 15-45 hours for fishing vessels, small freighters, and tankers, where greater variation in trim should be calculated and where curves of form are required.

Preliminary Design

To what extent preliminary design should be carried will vary with each individual. Without a doubt, the greater preliminary detail, the less adjustment of the final detail plans are required. Having established the physical qualities which bear on the design in question, omission of any quality results in an unsound conclusion. The suggested amount of detail would be the curve of areas and water plane, and wetted surface curves. From there on, all necessary information may be amassed to give complete data. It would not be amiss to mention here that standard girth parameters of ship sections are given in standard texts. Judiciously applied, these curves are an excellent quick and accurate aid in determining the wetted surface and are plotted B/H against sectional coefficient M.

It is well to remember that for a given displacement, wetted surface varies as the square root of the length. For similar section, girth varies as any linear dimensions such as beam, draft, or the square root of the area.

Length being usually well-defined, beam and draft are the only other dimensions where great latitudes and resulting changes in shape can occur. The shape of any hull, provided it is not abnormal, may assume infinite variations without increasing resistance, horsepower, displacement, etc. In using the non-dimensional curves, midship section has an exaggerated importance, and midship section is the controlling factor of all other sections as well as wetted surface, water plane area, displacement, etc. Since it can be proven that for a given displacement and length, there is little variation in wetted surface due to either changes in beam or draft, and that for given dimensions and displacements, wetted surface is affected very little by minor changes in shape, great latitudes in designing the midship section may be had without any adverse effects either in resistance or increase of horsepower.

Without a doubt, length is the largest controllable factor that affects wetted surface. Deadwood is the second largest factor, and during preliminary design may be dealt with rather severely with the view of lessening wetted surface. This applies mostly to sailing vessels and power vessels with large appendages. Quite often, struts, size of aperture, and other appendages may be dealt with in the preliminary stages. Wave and air resistance may be treated as the designer sees fit; however, when wave resistance is radically reduced, frictional resistance is radically increased.

Other Useful Curves

Other useful curves which would include SHP, resistance curves, frictional resistance curves, stability curves, etc., may be either dimensional or non-dimensional.

All racing rules governing sailing yachts may be plotted against a given base, usually L, which may be an actual hull measurement or a derived measurement. Such rules plotted on one sheet give instantaneous readings of a hull which has neither penalties nor credits. Occasionally, it is necessary to design in penalties to boost a given hull into a certain class; and at other times, it is necessary to design in credits to lower the rating of a given hull far below normal. When rule curves are utilized in place of mathematics, the raising or lowering, as well as determining base dimensions, reduces the amount of time normally consumed in preliminary design.

Tank Testing

The results of tank tests may also be included on the master or reference sheet since the majority of the information is in the non-dimensional. The importance of tank testing has in recent years been both exaggerated and minimized. Properly conducted tank tests are a valuable asset to the naval architect's files, especially if they are on his own designs, for he may then evaluate them according to other accurate data. However, many published results are the office "dogs," and comparison with these tend to elate the naval architect with the misguided belief that his new design has achieved great perfection.

Tank tests do not make a design good, nor do they in any way design a vessel; they do indicate exactly what the hull is. It is always desirable to have a series of hulls (3 or more)—each a modification of the other—so as to verify the results. Since this is rarely possible, even a vague similarity to each other will enable the designer to reduce the information to a common curve. In published results on small models where turbulence is not induced, the author is inclined to be rather doubtful of the results unless there is sufficient data of induced turbulence compared to bare hull over the same speed-length ratios, thus ascertaining the error in towing bare hulls.

Tank testing, and the resulting data, properly used, speed preliminary design; however, few owners are willing to accept the added expense of the test, and it is rarer still that a designer can afford to test models unless he is specializing in one type.

Hull weights, based on midship section weights, are very accurate especially if the midship section scantlings are based on the cube of the vessel, or if they vary with a linear dimension. Preliminary and final weights are undoubtedly one of the most important elements comprising a total design. It would certainly be convenient if all vessels could be weighed at various stages of construction to give the designer very accurate data on which to base preliminary assumptions.

Application to Actual Designs

The accompanying drawing and table illustrate the method outlined in this paper. The 31'-6½" surf boat was used as a parent hull, and the sectional area curve and design waterline were plotted in the non-dimensional form. It will be seen that the maximum section as well as the maximum beam of the waterline is in the vicinity of station 5.5. All stations are read as a function of unity. By substituting a dimension for unity, we may then integrate the new half-breadths and sectional area and arrive at displacement. Or we may integrate either or both curves in the non-dimensional, arriving at a multiplier which will, in substituting either midship section area or half-breadth of the water line, immediately give us displacement, water plane area, or any other of the attached coefficients. Drawing the curve of areas for each design on the same base allows one to superimpose other curves and immediately visualize the changes.

The first derivation of the parent hull is a 53'-0" coaster. The center of flotation has moved aft because of an increase in beam. The L/B has gone from 5.09 in the parent to 3.87 in the 53-footer, whereas the B/d has reduced

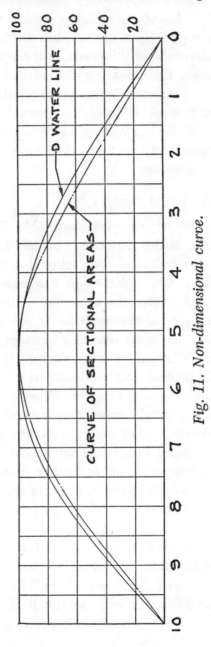

Fig. 11. Non-dimensional curve.

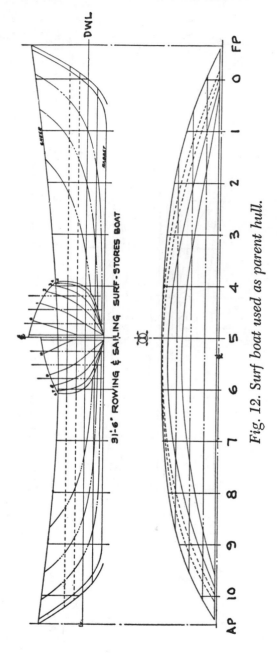

Fig. 12. Surf boat used as parent hull.

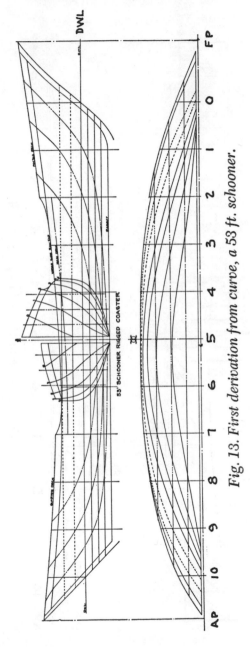

Fig. 13. First derivation from curve, a 53 ft. schooner.

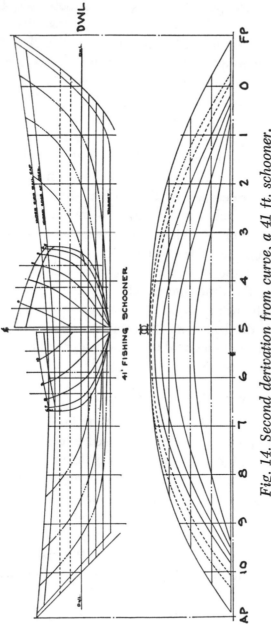

Fig. 14. Second derivation from curve, a 41 ft. schooner.

from 5.5 in the parent to 4.5 in the 53-footer, and the B/D is very close, there being only a few tenths difference.

The second derivation of the parent hull is a 41'-0" shoal draft fishing schooner. Her beam has again moved the center of flotation aft, and L/B is below 3, while the B/d is but .2 higher than the parent.

The primary purpose of this drawing was to illustrate the variety in shape which can be obtained, still retaining similarities of the parent hull. Similarities in the shape of sections was a matter of choice and not a matter of necessity. The preference of the author for the size of the curves is 20 inches in length by 5 inches in width, thus obtaining a curve which is relatively easy to draw and large enough to utilize "ducks" to advantage.

In any of the derivations, the bilges could have been harder or the draft increased beyond the ratios, or the center of buoyancy or flotation moved forward or aft with the same displacement. It unquestionably indicates the validity of such sectional area and water plane curves and the use of non-dimensional curves.

Using the Non-Dimensional Curves

Neither this article nor its author implies or suggests that non-dimensional curves be used to design any vessel, even though it can be done. This article does suggest the use of non-dimensional curves as a guide in preliminary design. The author always assumes that the designer knows what the requirements are and that, time permitting, the designer has several solutions that he would like to explore. As mentioned before, the non-dimensional curves permit the designer to evaluate all contemplated hull departures and shapes, as to any given initial shape.

In preliminary design, after the profile is sketched in to scale, thus ascertaining LOA, DWL, and draft, a tentative midship section must follow. By dimensioning waterline beam, extreme beam and midship section area, the designer may then refer to the non-dimensional curve and readily ascertain, by using an appropriate multiplier, displacement, B.M., C.B., water plane area, wetted surface, etc. Should there be a desired change in displacement or B.M., the midship section may be altered. Fixing displacement and B.M., the designer may then evaluate the design and fix scantlings which will evolve into actual hull weight.

The arrangement may then proceed, adding in weights and moments of major machinery groups, cargo handling gear, ballast, fuel, planking, etc., after which a final C.G. is determined. The C.G. may then be adjusted to the C.B. or the C.B. adjusted to the C.G. or both may be altered. In adjusting the C.B., the designer returns to the non-dimensional chart, altering the shape of the curve, but not the area, thus rapidly finalizing the entire design.

This sketch need not be more than a good freehand sketch. However, in the last steps, it behooves the designer to fair in, with curves, the deck and several sections as well as waterlines and perhaps a buttock and diagonal, thereby finalizing the design.

The sketch, as completed, guides, but of course does not restrict, the designer as to what is shown on the preliminary plan. As the designer progresses, refinements may suggest themselves, and should, of course, be incorporated into the finished design.

Summary

It is to the advantage of the naval architect to develop a system by which he may readily determine at the preliminary stages of design (the sketch) all pertinent design data, and may be able to integrate such changes as he desires, ascertaining immediately the effect of such changes.

Dimensional comparison of the characteristics at best is only a rough guess unless it is proportional to another vessel in all respects when the laws of similitude apply and dimensional comparison under these circumstances becomes a very accurate method of analysis. It is, however, restricted to vessels of similar type.

Dimensional comparison allows very little leeway as to hull form and hull ratios, and is, therefore, a restriction to the designer.

This method is perhaps the greatest handicap of all preliminary design systems in that similarity of hull shape is a must; therefore, the evolution of the hull more often regresses rather than progresses.

Non-dimensional characteristics can be very accurate. This method is quite fast and allows the designer great latitudes in hull shape and form. It is most useful when designing vessels of similar type, but in certain forms is equally adaptable to several forms of hull. It allows the designer to concentrate on any one function of design and enables him to adjust all others to suit without having to draw a complete lines plan or to begin any laborious calculations without first knowing the approximate results.

Addenda:

I may not have made it too clear that the designs are based upon a 31'-6" surf boat, and that the table indicates what was determined in the preliminary sketch as compared with what was determined in the final hull calculation.

One of the other interesting things that can be done with this type of curve is that it can be reversed and prismatic coefficient varied on vertical plots so that once determining the prismatic, the sectional area of each ordinate may be derived and the sectional area curve plotted. The varied systems that can be used with this are numerous, and I have tried them recently on a 770-foot tanker and find that they are to within about 2%. However, in such large ships, the block and prismatic are so great that there is an induced error in the system.

A fellow designer asked me if this were in any way based on the Colin Archer theory or any other mathematical pre-determined theory. It is not. The original curve is the result of the original design and all others are based on the original, which means that if the original were bad, subsequent designs would be inherently bad; and the same if the original were good. There is enough flexibility to change the characteristics of the hull by varying the location of the center of flotation or the center of buoyancy without changing the actual integrated area.

ITEM	PARENT		NO. 2		NO. 3	
	Prelim.	Actual	Prelim.	Actual	Prelim.	Actual
LOA	31'-6½"	31'-6½"	53'-8"	53'-8"	40'-9"	40'-9"
DWL	28'-0"	28'-0"	44'-0"	44'-0"	34'-0"	34'-0"
Beam WL	5'-6"	5'-6"	11'-0"	11'-0"	10'-10"	10'-10"
Beam Ext	6'-2"	6'-2"	11'-4½"	11'-4½"	11'-8"	11'-8"
Draft to						
Rabbet	1'-0"	1'-0"	2'-6¼"	2'-6¼"	2'-0"	2'-0"
L/B*	5.09	5.09	3.87	3.87	2.99	2.99
B/d*	5.5	5.5	4.51	4.51	5.68	5.68
B/D*	2.2	2.2	2.69	2.69	2.84	2.84
∇ Cu Ft	61.59	61.59	498.96	498.96	312.44	312.44
Δ Tons	1.759	1.759	14.26	14.26	8.93	8.93
Δ₁ Pounds	3942	3942	31933	31933	19996	19996
$\dfrac{\Delta}{\left(\dfrac{L}{100}\right)^3}$	80	80	167	167	227	227
C$_p$	.611	.611	.611	.611	.611	.611
C$_m$	.654	.654	.670	.670	.694	.694
C$_B$	.400	.400	.409	.409	.424	.424
C$_{WP}$	.640	.640	.640	.640	.641	.641
L.C.B.	.522	.522	.522	.522	.522	.522
MS. Area	3.60	3.60	18.56	18.56	15.04	15.04
WP Area	98.56	98.56	309.76	309.76	235.88	235.88
TPI	.235	.235	.738	.738	.562	.562
#PI	526	526	1653	1653	1258	1258
C.F. % DWL	.550	.550	.600	.600	.598	.598
Transv I	167	167	2103	2103	1556	1556
Long¹ I	3501	3501	22734	22734	10404	10404
MTI^{ton}/ft	.298	.298	1.23	1.23	.729	.729
MTI #/ft	667	667	2755	2755	1633	1633
BM$_T$	2.71	2.71	4.21	4.21	4.98	4.98
BM$_L$	56.84	56.84	45.56	45.56	33.30	33.30

* WL Beam
  L DWL

Chapter Eight

RELATIVE RESISTANCES OF SIMILAR ROUND AND V-BOTTOM MODELS

By LUTHER H. TARBOX

ONLY once in a blue moon does any designer get the opportunity to obtain exhaustive data on the comparative resistances of similar round bottom and V-bottom hulls. Even more rare is the chance to obtain such data on a round bottom and a V-bottom hull which are as similar in form and characteristics as humanly possible to make them. Back in 1946, the writer had a client for a 42-foot twin screw offshore power cruiser, who, while primarily interested in a hull design which could be built of plywood, also desired that the possibilities of a similar round bottom hull be thoroughly investigated with the idea that he would select the best resulting design for the building of his yacht. Plywood construction required a V-bottom hull with developable hull surface and, because of this developable surface requirement, it was decided to proceed with the design of the plywood hull as the first part of the design project. The client also decided that he wanted an additional alternate for the V-bottom design; a seam-battened hull for the third version. Each design alternate had to be fully evaluated by careful weight, c.g. and performance calculations.

It was decided early in the design stage that the most workable method of comparing the performances of the round and V-bottom versions was to build models of each and run carefully conducted model trials. The possibilities of turning this matter of model trials over to one of the better known tanks was considered, but this idea was discarded when it was found that the work could be performed only by two of the smaller tanks. It was felt that the results obtained from either would not be acceptably accurate by reason of the relatively inaccurate tank wall and tank bottom effects which would be present in any resistance data obtained from them. Also, only a relatively few runs would be made with each model. Any series of runs covering a fairly wide range of model speeds would be very expensive. Further, both tanks wanted models to a scale which conformed to the standards of a certain International Conference, which in the case of the design in question would have resulted in a very unsatisfactory sized model in the writer's opinion; both from the standpoint of reasonably accurate model resistance data and for reasons of possible future use of the models after the trials were run in the tank.

There was a still further disadvantage to running the trials in a tank; the tank model trials would be run in dead smooth water, a condition which would hardly ever be met with in the full-sized yacht. Therefore, a comparison of the relative performance and action of the two models in rough water was desired.

As the result of considerable discussion on the matter of the proposed model trials between the client and the writer, it was decided to have a round bottom and a V-bottom model built to 1/12th full size, i.e., to a scale of 1″ = 1′ 0″. It was further decided that the model trials would be run in relatively open water and rough water conditions and in a depth of water which would eliminate any prospect of shoal water effect in the resulting resistance data obtained. Models would be towed from a fairly long boom attached to a towing boat, the boom extending directly abeam and located far enough forward to insure that the towed model was well clear of the towing boat's bow wave.

To measure speed through the water, the writer's Aquaknot was to be used. This is a highly accurate speed measuring device which depends on the resistance of a towed weighted disc for its measurement and works on the beam scale principle. It is unfortunate that this instrument is no longer in production, having been discontinued early in World War II.

Model resistances were measured by means of an accurate surveyor's tension handle rigged with nylon fishline through a suitable system of sheaves; the tension handle being secured to towing boom adjacent to the mast. A postal scale had first been modified for use as a resistance scale but the first trial of this gadget indicated that it was much too sensitive, for it reacted sharply to engine vibrations aboard the towing boat.

The lines of the developable V-bottom hull were first

worked up and its plank surfaces formed of a multiple series of cones. The round bottom lines were simply the developable V-bottom lines with the chine knuckle well rounded off. This procedure gave a V-bottom boat and a round bottom with very similar hull characteristics. The waterlines were alike, so were the buttocks and diagonals with but the minor modifications in way of the chine of the V-bottom model. Preliminary weight and c.g. calculations were run for all three types of construction: the plywood hull, the seam-batten planked hull and the round bottom hull. These weight figures gave the desired model drafts at which the two models would be towed.

The V-bottom model was actually planked out in 1/6″ plywood, proving the correctness of the surface developability of the design. The round bottom model was built from a series of cutout ¾″ thick cypress lifts, glued up and then shaped to suit accurate molds for the model.

Provisions were made to eliminate the possibilities of resistance errors due to laminar flow after the fairly well accepted method developed at the Stevens Tank by means of sand strips located on each side of the stem of the model from a point a little above the waterline to a point slightly abaft where the stem joins the keel. Members desiring further information on the use of sand strips to create sufficient turbulence in the boundary layer to eliminate laminar flow effects or errors may find this information in a paper entitled "Some Experimental Studies of the Sailing Yacht" by Prof. Kenneth S. M. Davidson of the Stevens Tank, published in the 1936 Transactions of the S.N.A.M.E. For the models which are the subject of this paper, only two sand strips widths were used: ⅜″ and ¾″ and the complete series of model runs made with each

sand strip width. The correction for the additional resistances for sand strips is a very simple graphical correction.
Such a method of correction for this addition to total
model resistance is valid since the factor creating the
additional resistance is purely linear: that is, the area of
the ¾″ sand strips are just twice that of the ⅜″ sand strips.

The model trials were run under the close supervision
of the writer assisted by D. O. Hill and Dale Kroger,
naval architects, and a series of photographs of each
model run made by a professional photographer.

Careful record of the total model resistances were kept
on each model run and notes on behavior carefully calculated. Then the towline was carefully adjusted to make
the same angle with the waterline as did the shaft line.
Model distance off the side of the towing boat was carefully adjusted to insure that model ran ahead and well
clear of the towing boat's bow wave. Each model was
carefully adjusted to the designed trim flotation and to a
model draft corresponding to the proportionate model
displacement by the laws of similitude to the calculated
operating weight of the full-sized yacht. The calculated
weight for the round bottom design was greater than that
of the V-bottom design and the round bottom model first
ballasted to correspond to that draft giving the equivalant
displacement. However, the first run in open water with
the round bottom model indicated that the model would
not perform satisfactorily on this draft, towing was erratic, model rolled excessively, was wet and yawed considerably. Ballast was lightened until model performance
improved, the resultant reduction in model displacement
would have amounted to nearly two tons of displacement
in the completed yacht. The V-bottom model showed no

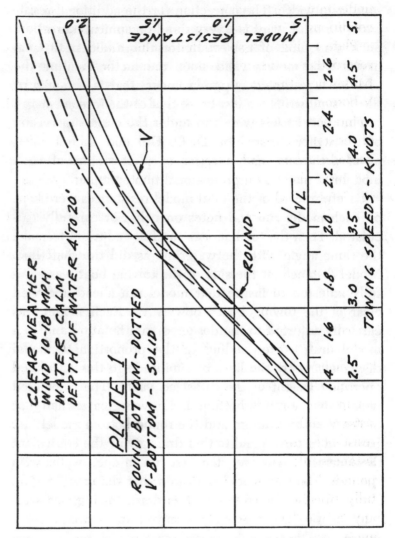

Fig. 15. Plate 1. Round and V-bottomed model resistances in moderately smooth water.

undesirable performance characteristics under the same
conditions of wind and water and on similar courses.

Plate 1 (Fig. 15) shows the resultant model resistances
recorded in moderately smooth water in the lee of the river
bank where the effects of wind resistance was negligible.
V-bottom model resistances were shown in solid lines and
round bottom resistances in dotted lines. The upper curve
of resistance in each case gives total model resistances recorded for runs made with ¾″ wide sand strips, the middle curve shows resistances with ⅜″ wide sand strips and
the lower curve shows total model resistances corrected
for sand strips. Both models were towed at the indicated
speeds by the dots or circles marked on the curves, viz:
2.5 kts, 3.0 kts, 4.0 kts and 4.5 kts. Corresponding speed
length ratios are indicated just above speed scale.

Briefly, the data desired from such model trials is to
obtain the wavemaking resistance data which may then
be used in the calculation of the resistance of the full-sized
yacht and thereby get a fairly acceptable prediction of
the yacht's performance. The method is simple: (1) Both
the model's displacement in tons and wetted surface in
square feet are calculated. (2) The model's frictional resistance in lbs. is calculated so that the model's frictional
resistances can be subtracted from the model's total resistances to obtain the model's wavemaking resistances in
pounds. The standard Froude formulation which is quite
fully explained in Skene's *Elements* is as good a method as
any to use. The figures for model's wavemaking resistances are then converted to wavemaking resistance in
pounds per ton (R_w/D) which then can be used in the
calculation of the full-sized yacht's wavemaking resistances.

Plate 1 is interesting since the curves clearly show the speed range in which the round bottom model should be superior from the standpoint of resistance to the V-bottom and vice-versa. In the design in question, the speed range where the round bottom model showed best was well below the desired operating speed range of the full-sized yacht. If the model resistance curves for the round bottom model had been obtained for the lower speeds, it would be seen that the total resistance curve was a series of humps and hollows, the hollows in the curve would be located at the corresponding speed-length ratios of .63, .72, .85, .114 and 1.114. At these points the round bottom hull's resistance will be less than the resistance of a similar V-bottom boat but at all other points of the speed range the resistance of the V-bottom hull will be less. Now again referring to the above speed-length ratios, there will be four waves alongside the boat at the first speed-length ratio, three waves alongside for the second, two waves for the third, and one wave alongside for the last. This interesting condition will be touched on later in this paper. However, it is important to note this obvious conclusion to this matter of the humps and hollows; if a certain low speed design has an operating speed which corresponds to a speed-length ratio where a hollow would occur in the resistance curve of a round bottom boat, a round bottom design *would be superior* on the powering angle to a V-bottom design, but, and note this well, at any other point on the speed curve the V-bottom design would be superior on the powering angle.

Please note, however, that the above remarks apply *only* where there are constant deadrise angles in the run in either a round bottom or a V-bottom design; or also, if there is increasing deadrise in the run in the case of slower speed designs. But all bets are off if there is but the slightest warp in the run, that is, decreasing deadrise angles in the run. The term "run" meaning the after quarter length of the hull in each case. Not only is this matter of deadrise angle in the run important at the higher speed ranges, particularly just below and within the "planing speed" ranges but also at speeds well below the higher speed brackets.

Again referring to Plate 1, there are several points which require further discussion. One item is the matter of the difference in wetted surface values for the round bottom design and V-bottom designs. The additional wetted surface of the round bottom design is due to the fact that the draft for the round bottom model was greater than that of the V-bottom model owing to the greater operating weight of the round bottom design. Yet, as previously stated, it was found almost impossible to tow the round bottom model at the required corresponding draft which would equal that of the full-size yacht because of the poor rough water performance of the round bottom model. Thus, insofar as the recorded model resistances show, the round bottom model actually has a slight advantage given it over the V-bottom since the V-bottom was found to perform satisfactorily at the design's operating draft in rough water.

The comparative rough water performances of the two models are of interest. The round bottom model was wet at anything but at the lower speed ranges, the roll was excessive, her pitching was more severe, and on downwind courses, the yawing was bad. The V-bottom model showed quite good results in rough water; she was far drier, both at the normal speeds where the round bottom model was comparatively dry, but at the higher speeds as well. She rolled less and pitched less. On downwind courses the yaw amplitude was not excessive, either at low or high speeds.

Even though the V-bottom hull proved superior to the round bottom hull for this particular design project, there are quite a few undesirable features in this V-bottom design. All are the result of the necessity for the developable plank surfaces required for plywood planking.

These items are: (1) Excessive wetted surface. Since wetted surface area is (when reduced to the simplest terms) simply the product of length times breadth, any departure from straight lines in either direction for a given overall size of surface increases the total resultant area. Now we cannot help having a curve in a fore and aft direction, especially for the bottom section lines. Straight bottom section lines would give the least wetted surface, therefore the use of either convex bottom sections (usual in all conic developments) or concave bottom section lines (so popular with many designers) will result in greater wetted surface area especially in way of the bottom where this is most important. The total resistance will be higher for either convex or concave bottom section lines since the wetted surface or frictional resistance increases with any increase in surface area.

(2) Convex bottom sections usually result in rather full bow sections which are much more likely to induce pounding within the higher speed ranges when in rough water.

(3) Convex bottom sections also give rather full water-

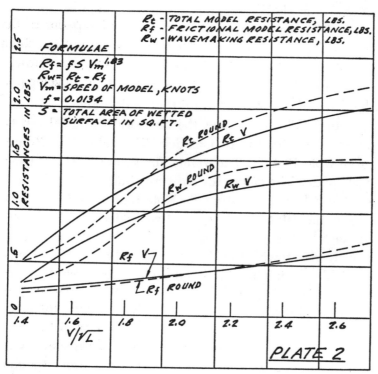

Fig. 16. Plate 2. Comparative resistance in pounds of
Round and V-bottomed models.

lines forward which result in somewhat higher wavemaking resistance both at low and at moderate speed.

(4) It is sometimes impossible to obtain a run free from warp in these developable hulls, and in most of this type, at least a moderate amount of warp will be present.

(5) The shape of the chine forward in both plan and profile often requires considerable modification in order to obtain the desired fair body line shape forward and it therefore follows that the designer has less control over the shape of the chine forward than is desirable.

Plate 2 (Fig. 16) shows the comparative model resistances in lbs. for the two models. The values for R_t are taken from Plate 1. The values for R_f are calculated for each model. The values for R_w were obtained by subtracting the values for R_f from R_t. Note that there is a difference in the values for R_f for the two models. This is due to the fact that at the higher speed-length ratios at which models were towed, the V-bottom model generated an appreciable planing lift which reduced her draft and thereby reduced her wetted surface; the reduction in W.S. being progressively greater as the speed increased. The W.S. values shown in Plate 2 are for the $V/\sqrt{L}$ point of 2.6. Compare the values of the hull coefficients. The only appreciable difference being in the value for displacement-length ratio which again shows the advantage given the round bottom model as the result of the forced decrease in model draft mentioned earlier in this paper. The resistance formulae are the standard Froude-Taylor formulation.

Plate 3 (Fig. 17) shows the final calculated brake horsepower curves for the round bottom and the V-bottom yachts. The R_w/D curves would show that the round bottom design was given an additional slight advantage in the

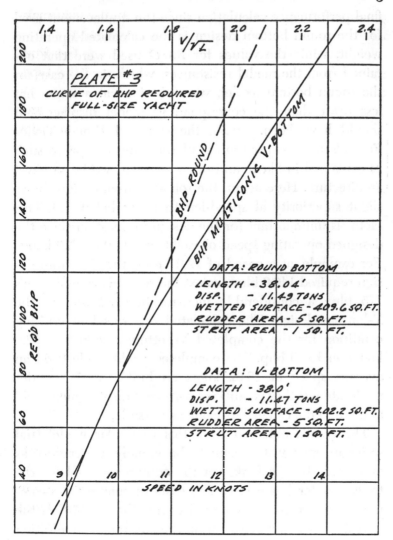

*Fig. 17. Plate 3. Final calculated brake horsepower curves
for the Round and V-bottomed yachts.*

final performance calculation since the displacement used for the round bottom design is the calculated operating weight, while the values for R_w/D used were that obtained from the model resistances, which, in the case for the round bottom model, were obtained at a somewhat less draft than the corresponding model displacement should have been. Again, the standard Froude-Taylor Formulation was used in calculating power required such as explained in Skene and other standard works on naval architecture. Here again, the round bottom design shows slight superiority at speed-length ratios below 1.6. This factor is unimportant for the design in question since the designed operating speed of yacht was 11.0 to 13.0 knots. For example, at a speed of 12.0 knots, the V-bottom design required 146.0 bhp against the round bottom design's 175 bhp; a considerable increase in efficiency for the V-bottom design. The calculated top speed in cruising condition for the completed V-bottom design was 12.4 knots on 158.0 bhp. The completed yacht made good an average speed of 13.02 knots on builder's trials under moderate weather conditions with trial displacement held as close to the calculated value as possible.

The results obtained from this particular model trial series in open water seem to be equally as accurate as obtainable from a tank, yet the equipment used for the trials was far less costly. The costs of running the complete series of trials amounted to less than a third of the lowest quotation received from the two tanks. In addition to the wavemaking resistance values which would have been the only data received from a tank, and then for only a narrow speed range, much additional valuable data was obtained in the relative performances of the two designs.

The writer is certain that many readers will be wondering about the fundamental reasons for the better performance of the V-bottom model over that of the round bottom model in question. By way of explanation, the writer offers the following comments for their consideration. These comments, the writer is most willing to point out, are for the most part purely personal opinion, though based on his observation and experience. Consequently, said comments will generate considerable disagreement on the part of many professional designers. The writer believes that the resulting discussion of the pros and cons are healthy for the profession, since such discussion may well spark additional experimentation which, in turn, may well result in a further increase in technical information on the subject of hull resistances.

The best reason why the V-bottom model resistances were lower in the moderate and upper speed ranges, in the writer's opinion, is that the chine knuckle acts as a plane of separation between the normal flow lines below the bottom of the hull between the chines and the disturbed flow lines above the chine along the sides of the hull; these lines of flow adjacent to the water surface being much disturbed by the normal wavemaking tendencies of the hull in motion. It is fundamental, in fluid mechanics, that a smooth, undisturbed water flow past any surface results in less resistance than when the flow is disturbed and erratic. Where round bottom hull forms are concerned, these surface wavemaking disturbances alongside the hull extend for a considerable distance below the surface with the result that the flow lines along the bilge are fluctuating and erratic. The same wavemaking disturbances alongside the V-bottom hull do not seem to upset the even smooth flow lines along the bottom below the chine; therefore, resistances normally should be less for this type with the qualification that they will be less only for speed-length ratios greater than 1.5 or 1.6.

However, there will be points along the speed curve at speed length ratios below 1.5 or so where the V-bottom resistances will be less than for the round bottom. These points are located at the humps in the R_w curves of the round bottom type, i.e., at speed-length ratios of 0.67, 0.781, 0.965, and 1.114. At the values of speed-length ratios previously mentioned in this paper, the round bottom resistances will be less. Of course, this applies only when round and V-bottom hulls are very similar both in characteristics and size. Now the hollows in the R_w curve for the round bottom hull will occur when the quarter wave is somewhat abaft the stern. The writer's views on the matter of the waves alongside and his comments on the speed-length ratios will be found to agree generally with most accepted authorities on the science of naval architecture.

Chapter Nine

MULTICONIC DEVELOPMENT OF HULL SURFACES

By SAMUEL S. RABL

ANY hull surface intended to be covered with sheet mate-rial—either metal, plywood or plastic, must be "develop-able." To be developable it must be either flat or curved to the surface of a cylinder or cone. Most developable hull surfaces are conic.

The popular conception of conic development is that the designer must choose one edge of his hull surface, select an apex point and design the other edge of the sur-face so that it will intersect radians to this apex. Thus, with a hull bottom as an example, either the keel or chine lines are drawn and the shape of the opposite line deter-mined by intersections with radians to the selected apex. This limits the designer to the choice of one line only.

The geometric theory that any curved line is composed of a multitude of short straight lines can be elaborated for hull surface development by the concept that the hull

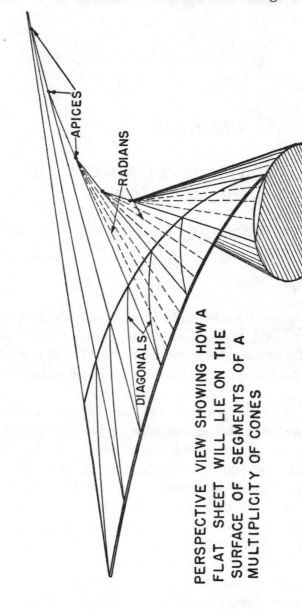

APICES

RADIANS

DIAGONALS

PERSPECTIVE VIEW SHOWING HOW A
FLAT SHEET WILL LIE ON THE
SURFACE OF SEGMENTS OF A
MULTIPLICITY OF CONES

Fig. 18. Conic development of a flat sheet.

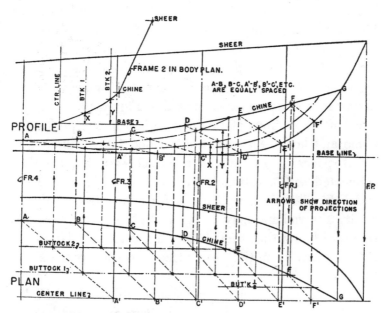

Fig. 19. Drawing the radians starting at the midships station.

surface is composed of segments of a multiplicity of cones having adjoining radians in common and whose apices lie somewhere out in space. For development purposes the location of these apices has no bearing on the final result. Figure 18.

To use the multiconic method, the designer lays down his lines in the time honored mode of drawing his profile and plan views. The next step is to draw the radians. As a general rule, the midship station is selected as the starting point and the first bottom radian A-A' is drawn to the first or second frame forward of this. Figure 19.

From the endings of this first radian in the profile the chine and keel-stem lines are divided into a number of equal spaces A to G and A' to G. These points are then connected with additional radians B-B', C-C', D-D', E-E', and F-F'. This equal spacing is for convenience only. In reality the radians may be spaced at random, the only requisite being that they follow a pattern similar to the ribs of a fan. From the profile these lines are projected to the plan as shown.

Convenient buttock lines are now drawn in the plan and their intersections with the radians projected back to the profile. From these intersections the trace of the buttocks may now be drawn. From the buttock heights in the profile, the shape of the bottom frames may be determined. (Example—X and Y on Frame 2.)

For topside development, water lines are used in lieu of the buttocks. Figure 20 and Figure 21.

It is often necessary to predetermine the shape of the hull covering sheets. This process is called "development." It is from this process that the expression "developable hull surfaces" originated. One of the more simple

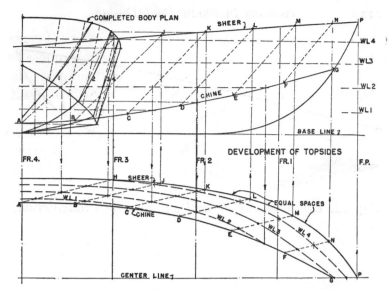

Fig. 20. *Topside development, using waterlines.*

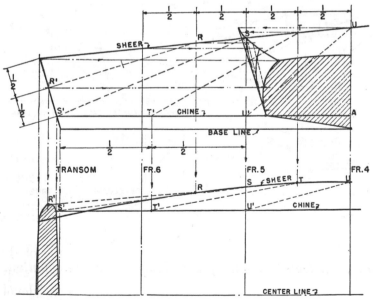

Fig. 21. *Further topside development.*

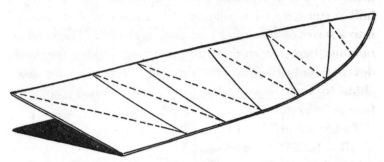

Fig. 22. Development of hull surfaces by triangulation.

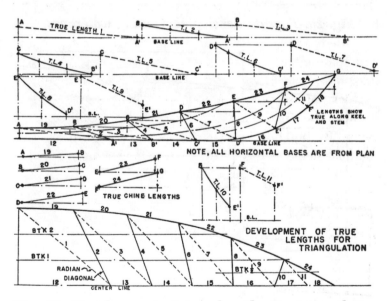

Fig. 23. Development of true lengths for triangulation.

methods of development is "triangulation." To develop a hull surface by triangulation the surface is first divided into a series of adjoining triangles. Figure 22. The original radians, being straight, form very good sides for these development triangles. By drawing diagonal lines from chine to keel between the radian intersections, the surface is "triangulated" for development. Figure 23.

To lay out or "develop" the hull surface the true lengths of all sides of all triangles must be determined. This is accomplished by the use of right triangles. The length of one side of these triangles, as they appear in the plan, is used for the base and their differences in elevation, as they appear in the profile, is used for the altitude. By laying out these two lines at right angles to each other the length of the hypotenuse, which is the true length, is determined. The true lengths are now used as radii of arcs which are intersected to form the final flat expansion. The diagonals, which are curved, are determined from the buttock intersections much in the same manner as the frames. Their true lengths are determined by girthing the curve. By building up the triangles in a continuous line, the final shape of the sheet is determined. Figure 24.

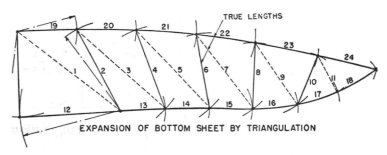

Fig. 24. Expansion of bottom sheet by triangulation.

While this method has been in use in the shipbuilding and aircraft industry for many years, it seems to be very little known by the small craft designers who need it most.

Chapter Ten

PROPELLER DETERMINATION

By GERALD T. WHITE

IN a day when we have airplanes speeding faster than sound it might seem that some genius could come up with a fool-proof formula for finding the correct diameter and pitch of a propeller. We have closely approached the point only when we consider that one of the factors in the formula is years of experience. That factor is one difficult to enter on your slide rule. It has been part of my task— perhaps my good fortune—to be so placed that I average about 1,000 propeller calculations a year; and that has been going on for many, many years.

I am still amazed at the abysmal ignorance of the layman when it comes to propeller selection. Only a fraction of boat owners turn to the naval architect or the propeller factor expert for advice. The remainder either pull the sizes out of a hat or rely upon the advice of a sincere, but utterly unskilled, salesman in an equipment store.

The unskilled invariably over-estimate the pitch in the

fond hope that the day of miracles is not past and that the boat will go faster than common sense indicates. They also underestimate the diameter with the feeling that the smaller wheel will allow a few more revolutions to be squeezed out of the engine. In a racing boat, extra revolutions may make the difference of a fraction of a mile an hour that wins the event. With the normal type of pleasure boat more revolutions often decrease the speed and invariably play hob with efficiency.

Much of the blame for this must be placed at the doors of the engine manufacturers. They have given us—whether we like it or not—super-speed engines. They protest to high heaven when we say that these engines are auto conversions. In many cases the engines were designed and built for marine service but the fact remains that they are of automotive design; even if not of automobile design. The piston speeds, valve travel and most of the other movements that involve wear are the same irrespective of whether the engine is in a boat, a car or running a generating plant.

Let us take, for example, almost any of the machines exhibited at recent Boat Shows. Their counterparts, in all essentials, will be found in automobiles. The machine that is rated 3,500 rpms for your boat will have its blood brother in your car. But when that engine is operated at 3,500 turns in your car the vehicle rolls along the highway at something like 100 miles an hour. Even the best special racing cars at Indianapolis have difficulty in maintaining such speeds for five hours. If you should run your car at 100 miles an hour for very long—assuming that you did not get pinched—the bus would soon go to pieces and the maker would laugh in your face if you asked him to make good on his guarantee. He would explain that no guarantees cover idiotic excess.

Yet the marine engine builders, in spite of their protests that their engines are real marine plants, often advocate similar piston speeds and general wear. They are perfectly correct in rating their engines at the peak rpms. To do otherwise would be accepting a handicap. But they are not justified in implying that the engine can deliver the peak speeds for any length of time. In fact some of the more honest ones do not advocate any such speeds except in light runabouts and hydroplanes which are the nautical equal of the track car. The makers freely agree that their engines should not be run at the very speeds at which they are rated.

Right at this point comes trouble. On the one hand they have sold their clients 100 hp at 3,600 rpms. On the other they have advocated a more reasonable rotative speed. But they know enough about human nature to realize that the man who buys 100 hp and 3,600 revs is going to get just that or scream that he has been gypped. The boat owner may not wish to run the engine at peak speed for more than a few minutes at a time; just long enough to impress his guests that the engine will do it. But to do that, even for a minute, requires that his propeller must be small enough to allow the top rotative speed.

That seems simple and logical to the owner. He compares his boat with his car. His car will do 100 but he seldom runs over 60. He forgets that his car wheels are reasonably efficient at all speeds from a highway crawl to the lonely road spurt. A marine propeller is only efficient at the speed it was designed to turn.

Barring loss of traction and wind resistance at high speeds the speed of a car is proportionate to the speed of the engine. For general argument we can say that the automobile that will do 90 miles at 3,000 rpms will do 45 miles at half that speed, and so on. But a boat does not increase in speed in direct proportion to the power, nor come anywhere near it. If we consider the average cruiser, not of the express type, it will have a peak critical speed of somewhere around 12 miles an hour. Power added beyond that point accomplishes little that can be considered efficiency from the engineer's standpoint.

To illustrate, I have taken as an example, a normal cruiser about 30 feet long and having a displacement of about 10,000 pounds. Using the most accurate speed formula I know of, I come up with the following speeds: With 20 hp, 8.25 miles. With 30 hp, 9.5 miles. With 40 hp, 10.5 miles. With 50 hp, 11.25 miles and with 60 hp, 12 miles. If we were running in direct proportion, based on the 20 hp speed, we would have a 25-mile boat with 60 hp. Actually, we do not get quite half that much.

Thus, while horsepower development and rotative speeds are in more or less direct proportion; boat speeds are not in that proportion. Let us examine the fundamentals of propeller selection. Basically the power and the rotative speed determines the diameter of the wheel. The speed of the boat determines the pitch. The faster an engine turns the less diameter is possible but the more power is delivered. We have diameter varying inversely as the rotative speed and the power.

Let us turn again to the boat used in our example. With 20 hp at 1,000 she would need a three blade 18 by 12 wheel. With 60 hp at 3,000 she would swing a three blade 12 by 7 wheel. You have a variation of about 1.5 in the required diameters and of about 2 in the required pitches.

It is considered a good rule of thumb to run a high speed engine at only 66% of her top rated speed under normal cruising conditions. Adopting that rule for our example we would need a 12 by 7 for 3,000 but a 14 by 8½ for 2,000 revs. The pitch speed with zero slip of a 7-inch pitch at 3,000 is 20 miles. The pitch speed of an 8½-inch wheel at 2,000 is 16 miles. If we fit the boat with a wheel to allow 3,000 turns we must use the 7-inch pitch or very close to it. When we slow that wheel down to 2,000, the recommended cruising speed, we get a pitch speed of 13.3 miles. But if the boat was fitted with the propeller for 2,000 rpms the pitch speed would be 16 miles. Puzzle; what happened to the lost 2.66 miles an hour?

Actually it isn't a puzzle at all. That 2.66 miles in pitch speed—call it 2 miles of actual speed after deducting for slip—has been wasted just as completely as if the fuel had been poured over the side. That 2 miles in net loss has been wasted just to allow the owner to proudly point to his tachometer and its rating of 3,000 revs. On a ten-hour run he has lost 20 miles of sailing just for the sake of a minute or two of 3,000 rpm boasting.

I believe that this can be summed up in the broad statement that a propeller must be calculated for the maximum speed it will turn under service conditions. If it is the correct size it will be too large to be turned any faster. If it is small enough to be turned at the peak speed, it is then inefficient at all rotative speeds less than the peak.

When a client insists on a propeller that can be turned at the peak speed of the engine, he is taking a licking every instant he operates at any speed lower than peak. To gain the ultimate for any occasional spurt he must learn to live with inefficiency the rest of the time.

All of this is easy to prove for the average boat. All you need to do is to figure propellers at various power developments. The situation also prevails in high-speed craft but not to so marked an extent. The lower the critical speed of the boat, the more the loss at cruising rpms. In spite of all the claims you will find at the Boat Shows, there are few real cruisers on the floor that have critical speeds of over 12 miles an hour. Some of them can be driven faster but the added power necessary is out of all reason from an engineering standpoint. It follows that the loss in efficiency we have discussed becomes greater, never less, whenever a boat is overpowered for speeds beyond its critical point. The speed curve for the boat we have used as an example peaks off at about 14 miles. Any such speed is considered peanuts at the Boat Shows where they look you in the eye and murmur something about 24 miles.

In approaching the problem of propeller determination there are four vital factors. (A) The horsepower. (B) The revolutions at which that power is obtained. (C) The speed the boat will make with the power specified and, (D) The size of the propeller aperture. In a new design, we can create the stern to allow for the proper size of wheel. But when the problem involves a boat already built, the aperture dimensions may prove to be the stumbling block.

Not one of these four factors can be ignored in your

calculations. If you guess at any of them the eventual success of the recommended wheel is a testimonial to your guessing ability more than your stature as an engineer. Yet, in practice, vitally needed information is either lacking or else comes from unreliable sources.

Time after time we are asked to provide a better propeller when the information furnished shows that the boat is running with a zero slip. And still the owner wants more speed! You may be amused at the prepaid cablegram I once received from Australia. It read, "Cable our expense proper propeller size for cabin boat with auto engine." Not one single word of any value in answering their question.

When information is lacking, or comes from unreliable sources, it is usually advisable to greatly underrate all the claims. Too many boats are timed by their proud owners over the course that stretches from the old wrecked dock to Simpkin's Point. The old-timers will tell you that the distance has been considered a mile since grandpaw was a boy.

There is another, and quite serious, aspect of propeller determination. I uncover no trade secrets when I tell you that the speed claims for most standardized boats are fantastic. Mr. Jones, let us say, buys a boat said to do 23 miles. He sincerely believes that it will do so. Someday he runs an accurate test and finds that the speed is way under the claims. He feels certain the propeller must be bent and comes to you for a wheel that will give him the 23 miles. You are now in a jam. If you, as a naval architect, tell him that no wheel ever made will drive her at 23 miles he is apt to reply that you do not know your business. He may even complain to the boat factory about your statement. Immediately they will put the clincher on the matter by informing him that neither you, nor your ancestors to the tenth generation, ever knew anything about a boat. In either case you are pictured as a second-grade moron because you told the truth.

An equally disturbing case is the tachometer jockey. He is the owner who bases everything on rpms. If he has an efficient wheel turning at 2,600 he will praise you to the skies if you recommend an inefficient one just as long as it turns 3,000 on the tachometer. But to suit him you must enter into a fraud. You are killing his efficiency to suit his vanity.

No discussion of propellers would be possible without mention of reduction gears. No item has been more of a blessing, or more of a curse. There is but one objective of a reduction gear. It is a method of making an unsuitable power plant work in a boat. It is a means of binding up your wounds, not something that will prevent you from getting hurt.

For every boat there is a minimum amount of blade area required. For normal purposes, we rate blade area in terms of diameter. The faster the engine the smaller the diameter until we reach the point—except in racing hulls—where the required wheel does not have enough area to push the boat. If we increase the diameter we slow down the engine and cut the power. The reduction gear provides us with the means of allowing the engine to turn fast enough to develop the needed power yet allow us to use a propeller diameter large enough to suit the boat. All this is rudimentary, but it has tripped up hundreds of owners and just about as many equipment salesmen.

The owner fits a fast engine to a relatively heavy boat. In dead smooth water, and with a light load, she may go along fairly well but when bucking wind or seas her performance falls off badly. Someone tells the owner that he needs a reduction gear. It sounds reasonable. Does he not get more pulling power out of his car when he drops into second?

He buys the gear, often taking one the salesman has on the floor. Off it goes to the boat shop where a mechanic tears out the old installation, possibly changes the beds, and installs the nice, new gear. The cost is a bit steep but the owner is quite happy to think of the bettered performance he will get. About that time he is slipped the sad news that the gear will require a new propeller. This is a further shot in the pocketbook but he is in so deep now there is no turning back. He writes the propeller company and is told that he needs an 18 by 16 wheel. He orders it shipped air mail to the boat shop. Then comes the sad awakening. On an otherwise bright and sunny morning the boat shop calls him up and sweetly inquires how they are supposed to fit an 18-inch propeller in a 14-inch hole.

Allow me to point out what happens to propeller diameters when gears are installed. We will assume an engine of 80 hp at 3,000 rpm.

Here are the required diameters:

Direct Drive	12 inch
1.5:1	16
2:1	19
2.5:1	22
3:1	24
4:1	29

I'll admit that I have not allowed for the reduced power caused by gear loss but the difference in diameters will be negligible. Yet, I have a record of an actual case where a reduction gear with 4:1 ratio was shipped by air freight from our Mid-West to Alaska for use in a boat that had room for nothing larger than a 14-inch propeller; yet that gear required a 26-inch wheel. Perhaps it is ironical that the poor owner, already stuck for hundreds of dollars, had to pay me for telling him he was in a jam. Until then, he had believed that a gear had some magic that would make his old 14-inch wheel become a plow horse instead of an egg beater.

These points are brought out to stress the fact that we have a far greater duty than just the preparation of good designs. We must constantly inform the boating public that any boat is a highly complicated mechanism requiring the attention of skilled technicians from the time it begins as a base line on paper until it is finally abandoned on the beach, having served its owner well throughout that span. Until we all put that idea across we will still be faced with the man who hesitates to take the crystal off his watch to clean its face but who will gleefully risk his money and his life monkeying with a far more complex and temperamental object—his boat.

Chapter Eleven

SOME NOTES
ON PROPELLER PERFORMANCE

By GERALD T. WHITE

IN spite of efforts dating back over many years the mathematical approach to the determination of the proper propeller for the not-quite-average small craft is still far from perfection. Thus, the engineer looks to performance tests as the best possible way to enhance his experience factor.

Often this seems simpler than it is. It is axiomatic that the delivery date for a new boat is invariably later than it should be. Owners finally reach the point where they are satisfied to get the boat into service. If the architect then comes along and wants to make exhaustive propeller tests, the owner has a fit about the delay. There is also the item of cost. Propellers are becoming more and more expensive with each passing day. Obviously, any series of tests must be time consuming and must involve trials with wheels of slightly different sizes. Who is to pay for all of this? Few owners are willing to carry the financial load, for they argue with some logic, that they already have paid the architect for expert advice. They feel that the extra cost of experimentation should be assumed by the designer. There are many cases where the cost of several propellers for a good-sized boat would just about equal the fee received for the design. In the case of a stock design the average cost would not pay for even a single propeller. The builder washes his hands of the problem just as long as he has installed the wheel recommended by the architect.

The total effect is that hundreds of boats go on and on with wheels that may be almost correct; in fact may even be mathematically correct; although little or nothing has been done to check up with a series of tests.

Standardized boats made by the better firms often do have test runs made but such results are not available to the public for reasons that should be obvious. But, even in these cases, it is generally agreed that propellers are fitted to give the engine maximum rpms in order that the last fraction of speed be squeezed out of the boat and that the engine revs up to its catalog rate.

To surmount these various obstacles is difficult unless you run across an owner who is so enthusiastic that he will go to the trouble and expense to make tests and collect data that is sufficiently accurate to be of interest to the engineer. Such a client is Mr. Minor Culli, a Floridian who owns a 28-foot V-bottom express cruiser built by Correct Craft and powered with a Gray Express Six-427. This machine is rated at 150 hp at 3,200 rpms and has direct drive. It is not the premise of this paper to discuss the problem on the basis that the power plant and the boat form an ideal combination. What we do hope to discuss with some value is what happened to this combination under quite exhaustive propeller trials.

Mr. Culli made a series of accurate tests of his boat and very kindly turned the results over to the writer as a basis for this paper. The accompanying curve sheet shows the results obtained with four different wheels. A fifth was also tried but the results appeared to be so poor that but one run was made. This wheel was the 16 by 10 that is indicated by a single spot on the graph. All wheels were made by Michigan and were of the regular three-blade pattern.

While the owner was, naturally, interested in boat speed as the final criterion, the chart was made up on the basis of slip losses. In other words on a basis of efficiency with the eventual speeds noted separately. Two of the wheels resulted in the identical boat speed, 19.35 mph. Our main interest is therefore to see how that top speed was obtained with the maximum overall efficiency, i.e., the minimum slip loss.

From calculations it appeared that the propeller should be a three blade 13.5 by 9.7. It is necessary to again call attention to the fact that no claim is made that the engine with direct drive is the best for the hull. Obviously, a wheel arrived at by formula and having a diameter of only 13.5 is not suitable for a boat of this character. A wheel 13.5 by 9.7 would be a special size so it would be usual to translate the fractions to a standard 14 by 9, or possibly, 14 by 10 wheel. This is in spite of the fact that a recently published formula for propeller diameter would call for 18 inches.

It has been the writer's experience that performance

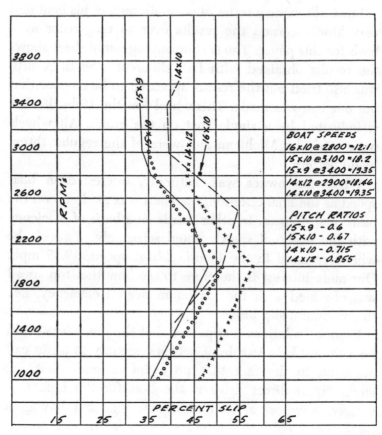

Fig. 25. Curves obtained with four different propellers.

usually benefits from increasing the diameter and, in many cases, reducing the pitch found by computation; this applying especially with overpowered boats. On that premise the most suitable wheel would be a three blade 15 by 9 when we consider only standard sizes.

If you will glance at the graph and recall that the curves are based on percentage of slip loss you will immediately see that each of the curves has a knee-like projection that comes about midway between the minimum and maximum operating rpms. In fact, three out of four of the wheels showed the greatest losses at 2,000 rpms; probably due to the increased resistance as the boat struggled to reach the so-called planing position. Even the fourth wheel, the 14 by 10, shows a break at the 2,000 rpm level although the losses increased up to the 2,500 rpm mark. Another interesting point in connection with this wheel is that it showed a slight increasing loss at the upper limits of the rpms. Once the other wheels had dropped back as the boat reached its running position the losses did not increase. But the 14 by 10 did slip more above 3,400 rpms. It would seem that this is due to excessive rotative speed and the beginning of cavitation. It can be accepted that the 14 by 10 was unquestionably too small for the boat in spite of the fact that it was one of the two wheels that produced the maximum of 19.35 mph.

The 15 by 9 propeller also gave a speed of 19.35 miles but it did so at 3,400 rpms while it took 200 more revs to get the same speed with the 14 by 10 wheel. This bears out the contention that adding diameter and decreasing pitch is of value in most cases. The pitch ratio of the 15 by 9 is .60 while that of the 14 by 10 is .715 according to slide rule.

Turning again to the chart, we find justification for the better results with the 15 by 9. With minor exceptions it showed the greatest efficiency throughout the entire rpm range. Its nearest competitor for this honor was the 15 by 10. Again we find that diameter seems to have more effect on efficiency than is generally accepted.

In this connection it might be pointed out that the average boat owner is a "tachometer-reader" and would prefer the 14 by 10 wheel on the assumption that the higher engine rpms proved it to be the best of the lot. Admittedly, this propeller did give the same maximum boat speed but, with few exceptions it is indicated as the least efficient of the wheels tested. The 15 by 9 shows the lowest loss at 1,000, 2,000, and 3,000 rpms. At only minor points does the second-best wheel show a better record. This second-best, the 15 by 10, fell down on final boat speed over a mile an hour.

Thus far every indication is that the 15 by 9 has a better efficiency throughout the rpm range as well as equaling the maximum boat speed. From this point on, we may leave the field of performance tests and enter into speculation of what might have happened had other propellers also been tested. The indications would point to a possible use of a three blade 15 by 8. However, there may be reason to believe that this wheel would allow too high rpms and that we would get into cavitation problems even though the bettered pitch ratio of .534 would help in holding cavitation back.

A 16 by 9 might improve conditions. Before accepting

that possibility, why not explore the problem of improving pitch ratio still more and, at the same time, holding the rpms to a point where engine wear is reduced and the possibilities of cavitation more doubtful? On that premise it would seem to the writer that some tests with a 16 by 9 with narrower blades might be worth the experiment. It is admitted that such a test would be a gamble but the curve of slip losses should be more nearly vertical with the result that, at varying rpms, the owner might have better general efficiency.

Obviously, Mr. Culli does not run continuously at 3,400 rpms. Engines cannot take such a beating hour after hour in relatively heavy boats. It follows that a reduction in slip losses at the more reasonable cruising speeds would be of more advantage than the fractional gain in speed at the upper—and seldom used—revolutions. The curves clearly indicate that the 15 by 9 propeller now has the best overall efficiency, yet we cannot but note with dismay that at 2,000 rpms the slip loss is 48% and the minimum loss 33%!

It was not many years ago that such losses would have caused the designer who was implicated to go forth and shoot himself. Today we are learning to live with such abnormal slips because boat owners have forgotten the cost of gasoline and insist upon overpowering almost every cruiser that is built.

The chart shows the usual distressing condition where the losses are greatest at the very point where the boat will be run most of the time; that is, around 2,000 rpms. At that point the fuel consumption per mile should be reasonable and the engine placed under no special stress.

There is no argument that this engine is not of the automotive type, rather than the classical marine type. The machine shows rpms as high as 3,600. If we translate that rotative speed into terms of automobile speed we can assume that the same basic type of engine in a car would produce a speed of around 90 miles an hour. Barring losses in traction and wind resistance, the same car would have a road speed of about 50 miles at 2,000 rpms. Who will question the fact that the average car is not designed to operate, year after year, at over 50 miles continuous speed?

Apply that to our propeller problems and we find that, at a rotative speed that would be reasonable for the engine, the slip losses are at their worst. This situation is not solely applicable to this boat of Mr. Culli's. It applies to virtually all of the standardized cruisers and, unhappily, to many of those that have been designed as custom jobs. The obvious cure would be to fit a propeller that had its maximum efficiency coincident with the rpms which were most suitable for long engine life and fuel economy. To do that in this boat would call for a much larger wheel than was tried and all hopes of rpms above the efficient point would have to be abandoned. Note, in particular, that Mr. Culli abandoned tests with the 16 by 10 wheel because he only managed to get 2,800 rpms with it. Yet, from an engineering point of view, the 2,800 revolutions were far higher than the combination of boat, engine, efficiency and economy would indicate.

It follows that the boat is now operating to the satisfaction of the owner—the various tests prove his sincerity and his willingness to experiment—but, on the other hand, the naval architect must deplore any trend in design which produces such results as we see on the graph. Carry the point a step further: What would have happened if Mr. Culli was not so thorough in his experiments? Nine out of ten owners would have used the 14 by 10 wheel because it produced the highest rpms, yet the slip losses would have run over 40%—a figure that means that about one-third of the fuel placed into the tanks produces no more real work than would have been the case had it been poured down the nearest drain.

If there is any virtue in this report of actual tests it would be that the designer of overpowered boats is least liable to err if he considers increasing diameters over those found by any of the well-accepted formulas. And, coincident with the larger diameter, he should be most hesitant about using as much pitch as is indicated by computation. These suggestions do not indicate that the various methods of computation are incorrect; that all we need is a new formula giving increased diameters and lowered pitches. Such a formula would fall down badly as used on what we still prefer to call a normal boat. In the cases where the computations underestimate diameter and overrate pitch, it is inevitable that we also find a boat that is being driven above her critical speed. In other words, the overpowered boat that is so dear to the heart of the standardized builders and so equally dear (using the word in its other sense) to the pocketbook of the boat owner.

In closing, allow me to extend cordial thanks to Mr. Culli for the careful preparation of the tests; a series which involved a great deal of time and expense. The tests were certainly worth the effort to him. But what about the owners who accept boats that are wheeled with what the boat dealer thinks is correct? Can we blame them if they give up the sport after a year or so?

Chapter Twelve

THE STABILITY OF POWERBOATS

By CHARLES W. WITTHOLZ

THE PROBLEM: We have all seen, read and studied magazine articles, textbooks and papers on the subject of stability. In almost every instance the text gave the elements of stability and numerous other relations bearing on the problem. The calculations involved in determining the CG, CB, BM, etc. have been well covered in textbooks, as has also the determination of GM by means of a Stability Test or Inclining Experiment.

The foregoing information is all a necessary part of a naval architect's education, and certainly it should be known equally as well by the small craft designer. But isn't it strange that almost no one has written an article on how much stability a power boat should have? At the present time, there is no yardstick to determine whether a given boat definitely has too much or too little stability. We're in a position where we can calculate stability, but don't really know whether we have the right answer or not.

So the purpose of this article is to discuss how much stability a powerboat should have, rather than how it should be calculated.

Analysis of the Problem: Before going further, let me state first that this discussion is limited to mechanically propelled boats up to 65 feet in length, less than 75 gross tons, carrying 49 or less passengers, and not engaged in ferry service; secondly, that the amount of stability required should be present in the boat when the hull is intact and without the bilges, cockpit or any compartment appreciably flooded; third, that the stability required has to be referred to the number of persons on board and the most adverse wind and wave effect for the waters she is designed to operate in and, fourth, is not concerned with compartmentation or flotation devices.

Facts Bearing on the Problem: Essentially, the satisfactory solution to this problem results in a boat which will have sufficient stability to safeguard the lives of those on board. Actually, the answer is complicated by the following facts:

Small open craft can easily be over-powered and capsized or pitch-poled in heavy weather.

Open boats can be swamped and sunk without capsizing, regardless of how much stability they have.

As the boat becomes smaller, the weight and VCG of the crew becomes more and more important in influencing stability.

A certain amount of bilge water causing reduction in GM is present in many boats.

W.T. cockpits can easily be flooded with attendant reduction in *GM*.

Analysis of the Facts: An accurate analysis of the preceding facts involves discussion with numerous naval architects, boat owners and government regulatory agencies which I have not as yet had time to do completely. Later on, I will mention whatever data I have so far obtained.

Before going into that, we might analyze the general aspects of the problem at this point:

The fact that small open craft such as rowboats, outboard motor boats and small inboard skiffs can easily be overpowered, requires special consideration as to minimum freeboard, volume of the boat and stability. In considering small craft, a weather limitation must also be established. While it is certain that many wooden boats remain afloat after capsizing, due to the mean density of engine and hull being less than water, it is not believed correct to assume any hull whatever to be outside of the requirement of stability due to her floatability when swamped or capsized.

The history of small boat casualties shows cases where small craft have been thrown end-over-end by large waves. This pitch-poling is believed to be a factor beyond the scope of this discussion due to it being concerned with longitudinal stability and it being, perhaps, an unavoidable hazard akin to automotive driving.

It should be noted that the S.S.C.D. has on May 24th, 1950 adapted a code of performance which designates hulls as follows:

Type O (Ocean-going)   Rating 2000 or more
Type C (Coastwise)   Rating 1500 to 2000
Type B (Bay and Harbor) . Rating 850 to 1500
Type R (River)   Rating 500 to 850
Type S (Speed)   Rating 500 or less

For each of these types, we might determine a stability criterion or have a fixed criterion and limit the waters.

Since the weight of the crew and its vertical position relative to the CG of the boat is so important in changing the GM of small craft, it is necessary to include a definite limit in the quantity of the crew and to consider their approximate vertical position in the boat.

Regarding bilge water, the great reduction in GM possible in small craft and cruisers due to free bilge water and partially flooded W.T. cockpits demands attention, since these areas can be flooded on any of the boats under consideration without necessarily approaching an abnormal operating condition.

Opinions: Before I propose a formula for obtaining the correct stability of a power boat, I would like to give you a little of the background of the present day comments on this subject.

I have discussed this problem at random over the course of years and have had the following comments from various designers:

"I don't know what the stability of this 28-foot skiff is, but I have an idea she has a GM of from 12 to 14 feet."

"Power boats in general have so much more stability than they require that I never calculate it."

"I purposely gave this 65-foot patrol boat one foot more beam than I would an equivalent sized yacht since I believe this boat might be used for rescue work and should remain upright with 65 men on one side. I study the stability of every power boat I design."

I have also discussed this problem with our chairman, Mr. White, who thought the problem was a good one for a paper and that he was convinced that many small outboard cruisers were unsafe due to high deck houses, insufficient weight and the fact that two or three of the crew often sat or sunned themselves on top of the trunk cabin, sedan house, or housetop thereby greatly decreasing the GM.

In the April, 1954 issue of the *Proceedings of the Merchant Marine Council* there appeared an article entitled "A Glance at Outboard Motor-boating Calls for a Second Look." I wish to quote the contents of this article to emphasize the importance of doing something about this problem.

"During fiscal year 1953, 69 outboard motorboat accidents involving the loss of 109 lives were reported to and investigated by the Coast Guard opposed to 24 accidents with the loss of 36 lives in fiscal year 1952.

"A typical accident involving an outboard motorboat where the loss of life was somewhat higher than usual was the case of a family who, after finishing their picnic supper, decided to go across a navigable lake in a small outboard motorboat. The family, 10 in number,

boarded the boat which shortly after departure capsized and 9 of the 10 occupants drowned. The boat was
provided with no life-saving devices. The sole survivor
stated: 'Without any warning or apparent cause the
boat sank suddenly; 9 out of the 10 persons in the boat
were drowned. I was the only survivor. Prior to that
time there had been no indication that there was anything wrong with the boat.'

"In a similar casualty of overloading where no life-
saving devices of any type were carried and 5 persons
were drowned, the owner-operator stated: 'I loaded the
boat with 7 passengers and proceeded upstream for a
short ride. About a mile upstream one of the passengers
complained that her child was cold. I immediately shut
the throttle of the motor down to minimum and proceeded to make a turn to return. As the boat upon its
return approached the wake, which we had created as
we went upstream, water entered the boat over the
bow, causing a panic as near as I can remember
amongst them, thereby capsizing the boat.' "

The Coast Guard has referred this latter case, as well as
other similar cases, where the operator has survived to
the U.S. Attorney General for criminal prosecution for
reckless operation of a motorboat and manslaughter.
Whether or not an operator survives so that he may be
criminally prosecuted or whether or not any convictions
are obtained, the fact remains that nothing can bring
back the lives of those lost while under his charge.

The state of mind of the above survivors, as evidenced
by their statements, clearly indicates their complete
lack of acquaintance with or knowledge about any or

all rudiments of boat safety or safety afloat. In a word, ignorance was the cause of the casualty in which they were involved. A review of the record indicates that this is true of virtually all outboard motor accidents involving loss of life. The cause for the appalling loss of life in outboard motorboat accidents in their order of importance may be classified as follows:

1. Irresponsibility and overloading
2. Operation under bad weather conditions
3. Failure to carry U.S.C.G. approved life-saving devices for each person on board
4. Failure to become indoctrinated with or make provision for the use and availability of lifesaving devices under emergency conditions
5. Reckless navigation, i.e., no lookout; following other vessels' wakes, etc.
6. Speed
7. Lack of knowledge of basic seamanship

Indications are that operation of outboard motorboats is on an upward surge so that an increase of accidents of such motorboats involving a loss of life may be expected unless energetic preventive action is instituted.

We all know that outboard motorboat operators require no licensing and that the boat itself is subject to only the minimum legal safety requirements. Some action which is at least a wedge of common sense into the ignorance and irresponsibility of outboard motorboat operators is strongly indicated in the interests of preventing needless loss of life.

To create such a wedge, consideration should be given to the following suggestions:

Furnish each purchaser or lessee of an outboard motor or boat with a pamphlet pertaining to the elements and rudiments of safe motor boat operation and safety afloat.

Permanently indicate on each outboard motor boat the legal and real necessity for carrying approved life-saving devices, including methods of use and availability.

Construct boats intended for use with outboard motors with built-in air tanks filled with a suitable buoyant agent such as balsawood, kapok, cork, etc.

In each boat, attach a permanently legible plate clearly setting forth the maximum capacity of the boat, the minimum freeboard of the boat and the weather conditions under which the boat may be safely operated.

By contrast with the above cases there are many accounts of long voyages in short boats which show how remarkably able a very small boat can be. Obviously the typical boat of today is not designed for such purposes.

I spoke to another naval architect about this problem and he referred me to the U.S. Coast Guard publication CG-256 *Rules and Regulations for Passenger Vessels.* Shortly thereafter I was aboard a Maritime Commission C-4 class ship for a stability test. At that time I discussed the problem with Commander Coyle, U.S. Coast Guard New York office, who specializes in these problems for merchant ships. I noted that there had been a number of articles dealing with proposed legislation for the stability of small commercial fishing and party boats in *Atlantic Fisherman* for April, 1954, *Newsday* of March 26, 1954, *Newsday* of April 1, 1954.

I followed this up with a letter to the U.S. Coast Guard in Washington, mentioned the pending legislation and requesting information as to what their present recommendations were for small craft and what they proposed for party fishermen. Captain C. P. Murphy, Chief of the Merchant Marine Technical Division, replied as follows:

"We have your letter of 6 August 1954 concerning stability criterion for small craft and requesting that you be placed on the mailing list for the 'Proceedings of the Merchant Marine Council,' which is being done.

"Enclosed for your information is a copy of the 'Rules and Regulations for Passenger Vessels, CG-256, dated November 19, 1952, which are applicable to all passenger vessels over 15 gross tons. Section 75-10 of these regulations contains the stability standards which are normally applied to inspected passenger vessels above the aforesaid tonnage limits and which, it is believed, can be used, with some exception in certain cases, in the assessment of minimum required stability for smaller craft.

"We should be very glad to receive a copy of the paper which you indicate you expect to deliver on the subject of small craft stability and to have any comments which you may care to make concerning the usefulness of the standards given in Section 74-10."

At the second session of the United Nations sponsored International Fishing Boat Congress in Miami in November 1953 Mr. George C. Nickum presented an interesting paper on "The Stability of Fishing Vessels." It covers approximately 12 pages and states that fishing vessels have suffered numerous casualties and are now so complex as to merit serious thought about establishing a standard. His premise is that First; such a criterion must enable a designer to forecast a new vessel's compliance with the criterion without requiring elaborate and expensive calculations. Secondly, the criterion must be so set up that simple tests by relatively untrained personnel can verify the compliance of any fishing vessel with the criterion without requiring the availability of design plans.

Conclusion: The conclusions which have so far been made public are formulae for indication the required *GM* and/or freeboard or buoyancy for the given class of boat.

1. CG-256 gives two criterions for passenger vessels: the weather criteria being:

$$\text{GM equals } \frac{P \, A \, h}{D \tan \phi}$$

where P equals $.005 + \left(\dfrac{L}{14,200}\right)^2$ tons/ft²

for ocean and coastwise service.

and P equals $.0033 \left(\dfrac{L}{14,200}\right)^2$ tons/ft²

for partially protected waters such as lakes, bays and sounds

and P equals $.0025 \left(\dfrac{L}{14,200}\right)^2$ tons/ft²

for protected waters such as rivers, harbors, etc.

L equals Length between Perpendiculars
A equals Projected lateral area in square feet of portion of vessel above waterline
h equals Vertical distance in feet from center of *A* to center of underwater lateral area or approximately one-half draft point.
D equals Displacement in long tons

ϕ equals Angle of heel to $\frac{1}{2}$ the freeboard to the deck edge or 14 degrees, whichever is less.

And the Passenger Criteria being:

$$\text{GM equals } \frac{N \times b}{24\ D \tan \phi}$$

where N equals number of passengers

b equals distance in feet from the vessel's centerline to the geometrical center of the passenger deck area on one side of the centerline. It should be noted that each criterion is figured separately and the maximum used. They are not combined effects.

2. Mr. George C. Nickum recommends for fishing vessels; that

(a) The vessel, in its most severe operating condition must have the following characteristics:

(1) GM equals to or greater than .10B or 2 feet

(2) $\dfrac{F}{B} + \dfrac{F}{L \times B}$ equals to or greater than .15

Where: GM equals metacentric height

B equals maximum beam over planking or plating at the waterline

F equals the freeboard in feet from the waterline to the edge of the freeboard deck at the side, measured amidships.

FA equals freeboard area in square feet (projected on a vertical plane through the centerline) between the waterline and the freeboard deck at side.

L equals the registered length

(b) Compliance with the above characteristics must be proven by physical measurements with the vessel in its most severe operating condition. *GM* is to be calculated from actual measurements of period of roll in this condition using the following formula:

$$\text{GM equals } \frac{MB}{T}2$$

where *m* equals .40

3. As yet I know of no other proposals and no legislation on the stability of powerboats that has become law.

Recommendations: I have endeavored to investigate the validity of the foregoing rules for small craft. As an example I have chosen a 23-foot sea skiff as representative of one size of boat the small craft designers would be interested in.

By entering the required data into the various formulas, I obtained the following required *GM:*

23′ Sea Skiff

By U.S.C.G.:

Weather GM equals $\dfrac{P\,A\,h}{D \tan \phi}$

$$\text{equals } \frac{.005 + \dfrac{23}{14,200}\,2 \times 73.67 \times 2.30}{1.75 \tan 14°}$$

$$\text{equals } \frac{.005 \times 169}{1.75 \times .2493} \text{ equals } \frac{.345}{.436} \text{ equals } 1.93′$$

(assuming ocean going factors)

Passenger GM equals $\dfrac{N \times b}{24\, D \tan \phi}$ for ocean and coastwise

equals $\dfrac{10 \times 1.55}{24 \times 1.75\, \dfrac{150 \times 10}{2240} \times .2493}$

equals $\dfrac{15.5}{24 \times 2.42 \times .2493}$ equals $\dfrac{15.5}{14.48}$

equals 1.07' (ocean)
(assuming 10 passengers)

By George C. Nickum:

GM equals to at least 2 feet
$F/B + FA/LB$ equals .15 or more
$2.8/6.7 + 64/22 \times 6.7$ equals $.418 + .43$ equals .85

The actual GM of this skiff is 3.45' by checking period of roll and by a stability test made after launching. This is greater than any of the present rules call for.

But I consider a boat of this type to be suitable for coastwise use only and not offshore work. I believe such a boat should be stable enough to withstand a combined weather and passenger effect of a 60 mile per hour wind, a partially flooded cockpit, and an off-center crew simultaneously without capsizing. (Note that simultaneous effects are not taken in the C.G. Rules.) A 60 mph wind causes a pressure of 12#/S.F. As a factor for half flooding of the cockpit, I decided to make it relative to the moment of inertia of one side of the cockpit as related to the total water plane. I chose to multiply the required *GM* by the length of the boat plus ½ the cockpit length divided by the length of the boat (thus assuming the mean width of the cockpit equal to the mean width of the waterplane).

For passenger criterion I used the Coast Guard figure, but multipled by 150# to obtain a heeling moment in foot pounds.

The resulting basic formula appears like this:

$$\text{GM equals } \frac{12\,Ah + 150\,Nb}{D5 \tan \phi} \times L + \frac{\frac{1}{2}}{L}$$

where A equals projected lateral area in square feet of hull and all deck houses

h equals vertical distance in feet from center of A to the center of the underwater lateral area

N equals number of passengers

b equals distance in feet from the boat's centerline to the geometric center of the cockpit and cabin floor on one side of the centerline

L equals length on waterline

l equals length of floor of cockpit

D equals displacement in pounds

ϕ equals angle of heel to $\frac{1}{2}$ the deck edge amidships or 14°, whichever is less.

Applying this to the 23-foot sea skiff it is discovered that the requirements are about met if 4 passengers are used:

GM equals

$$\frac{12 \times 73.67 \times 2.30 + 150 \times 4 \times 1.55}{4250 \times .2493}\frac{(21 + 5.25)}{21}$$

$$\text{equals } \frac{2030 + 930}{1060}\,(1.25) \text{ equals } 3.48'$$

I believe some such criterion as this closely resembles the required *GM* for coastwise power boats; and may possibly be used for boats up to 65 feet length, 49 passenger capacity, or 75 gross tons. I would like to see more wind heel requirement for ocean going boats together with less passenger heel but have not decided how much at this time. In small outboard cruisers and inboard cruisers the required *GM* should be increased by the V.C.G. rise where crew is often seated on the house or trunk top. This requires an addition to the *GM* of

$$\frac{N \times 150 \times h}{D + 150\,N}$$

Where *N* equals number of passengers on house top, and *h* equals CG of passengers above the CG of the boat.

For boats less than about 20′ LOA and any open boat I propose that they be considered practical for harbor and bay use only, and that a minimum freeboard amidships of L/20.5 feet in the maximum loaded condition be used together with certification by the designer on his plans for no more passengers than one tenth of the internal cubic capacity of the boat in feet.

In summary it might be pointed out that a formula is probably the only way to represent just what should be required of a given boat.

Both the Coast Guard rule and my own rule are based on righting moment (D GM tan ϕ as against wind heel ($P\,A\,h$) and passenger heel $N \times b \times 150$. The various services in the *CG* rules represent wind velocities of 58, 47, and 41 mph for ocean, bay and protected waters respectively. The $\dfrac{L}{14{,}200}$ 2 factor represents a velocity increase of 1 mph for each 7.23′ of boat length or 1#/ square foot pressure for each 125′ of boat length. The main difference between the U.S.C.G. Rule and my rule is that I use combined effects where the U.S.C.G. uses the maximum of either weather or passenger effect, taken singly.

Chapter Thirteen

NOTES ON THE CONVERSION
OF A RUNABOUT

By LUTHER H. TARBOX

PROBABLY one of the most disagreeable jobs which can befall a designer of yachts and small craft is an assignment calling for the conversion or alteration of an existing boat for service or use other than originally intended.

Usually, all sorts of difficulties crop up in the process of working up a conversion design. Far too often it is found that no plans whatsoever are in existence of the original boat, which results in the necessity of having the boat hauled out, then taking off lines from the hull, making numerous notes and sketches of the existing arrangement and of the hull structure and the taking, or having taken, a series of photographs of the boat from all angles. Also, it often is the case that the original design of the boat to be converted is more or less unsuitable for the intended alteration with the result that the converted boat is found to be an indifferent performer and her owner is almost sure to become dissatisfied with the job within a very short time after completion.

In view of the conditions attendant to a conversion design as outlined above, many designers avoid acceptance of conversion design commissions, especially after a few sad experiences with this class of engineering work.

Once in a great while, there will be a conversion design commission offered which has interesting possibilities and evidences a lack of at least some of the difficulties usually attendant to this class of design. Such was the case when the writer was commissioned to prepare a design for the conversion of a standardized 24' 6" utility runabout to an express day cruiser.

Many difficulties were present in so far as lack of required data was concerned. Correspondence with a former official of the now defunct manufacturer of the boat turned up the fact that no plans existed of this particular model produced by their firm and further, that there never had been lines or offsets of the boat prepared; the lines had been worked up full-size on the loft floor. This fact alone was sufficient proof that no engineering whatsoever had gone into the design of the boat in the first place, thus, calling for considerable caution in the preparation of any alteration or conversion design.

The owner was able to provide some information on the original boat in the form of the manufacturer's catalog, which contained considerable useful data such as the major scantlings, shipping weight, fuel tank capacity, a list of equipment, a list of optional power plants for the boat, together with shaft sizes, propeller sizes for the listed engines. It contained, in addition, fairly large and clear illustrations of the boat under construction in various stages and in the completed state. Reference to an old Show Number of *Motor Boating* gave further data on the original boat.

The owner had the boat hauled out and the boatyard operator took off the lines of the boat, paying particular attention to lifting accurate offsets for the heights and half-breadths of the chine and sheer. The profile of the stem and the rake and crown of the transom were carefully lifted from the boat. The exact amount of flare and flam in the topsides were relatively unimportant, so that shape in this area was not lifted. Also, in the original boat there was an extreme amount of concavity to the bottom sections in the forebody, dying out to a flat straight line at the underside of transom. Since the entire bottom below the chine would be redesigned, the actual shape of the bottom section lines were not lifted from the boat. The owner took a very nice series of photos, showing the boat out of water at all angles, which proved extremely useful in the development of the conversion design. Immediately after the lines were taken off, the scantlings were checked by the boatyard operator and listed. This check on the scantlings proved the correctness of the data listed in the manufacturer's catalog on this particular model.

The original 24' 6" boat (which had been acquired by the owner just a few months previous to his instructing the writer to prepare a conversion design) was powered with a single Chrysler Royal Standard Model direct drive engine, rated at 140 bhp at 3,200 rpm. The weight of the boat in loaded condition, driver only aboard, was approximately 3,800 lbs. This weight figure was arrived at from the data contained in the manufacturer's catalog and further checked by a displacement calculation of the lines of the original hull, which was drawn up from the offsets taken from the hull and from information contained in the photos of the boat. The load waterline on the boat was very noticeable in the photos. Since the owner had provided the negatives that he had taken of the boat, it was a simple matter to take one negative showing the boat viewed from a point directly off the beam amidships, insert it in an enlarger and focus the enlarger so that the image on the enlarger easel was to exact scale, then produce the enlargement. This enlargement gave the drafts of the boat by checking the position of the line of flotation very evident in the picture.

Both the characteristics of the original boat and of the express day cruiser conversion are given in the appended Table of Characteristics. In addition to the dimensions of the boat and displacements and power, approximate area of planing surface, aspect ratio of planing surface, unit power loading (displacement/bhp), unit planing load (displacment/area of planing surface), load coefficient, propeller size, speed and apparent slip are given.

The scantlings for the bottom framing and planking of the original boat left much to be desired. The concave bottom sections were the cause of considerable pounding in choppy water, say a 2 ft. to 3 ft. chop. The bottom planking, which was double diagonal, panted noticeably and at times, leaked moderately. The bottom planking was supported by fairly heavy web frames spaced 24" centers, and with light intermediate frames laid on the flat between web frames. The inner skin of the bottom planking was laid at approximately 45 deg. to the centerline, the outer skin laying fore and aft. Thus planked, the

bottom planking would contribute little to the longitudinal strength of the hull.

Consideration of the scantlings of the side planking,
which was seam-batten, and of the keel, clamps, planksheer, shelf and engine girders, indicated that the possibility that these members were not sufficient to provide
adequate longitudinal strength to absorb the rapid rever-
sal of hogging and sagging stresses met with in choppy
water at speed for the original hull. Therefore, a calculation for virtual weight of the original boat was made,
taking the speed at 32 mph and a wave height of 3 ft. The
section modulus of the original hull was then calculated
and checked against the required section modulus derived from the sagging moment, which in turn had been
derived from the virtual weight calculation.

It was found that in comparing the required section
modulus against the section modulus of the hull that the
theoretical safety factor of the original hull was less than
2 to 1; and while the writer would be the first to admit
that the outlined stress analysis is but roughly approximate, it is evident to the writer that the hull structure of
the original boat was on the weak side (even for the original power installed in the hull) and emphasized the lack
of engineering in the design of the original boat.

Since the owner desired the maximum possible performance in express day cruiser conversion and had selected for power, twin Chrysler Royal Specials, each
engine's maximum rated horsepower being 165 bhp at
3,600 rpm, it was obvious that the bottom lines would
require considerable alteration, both for the performance
desired and from the standpoint of required longitudinal
strength. The concave pounding bottom sections would

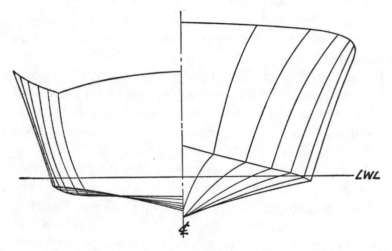

*Fig. 26. Original bottom lines of the 24 ft. 6 in., Gar Wood
utility.*

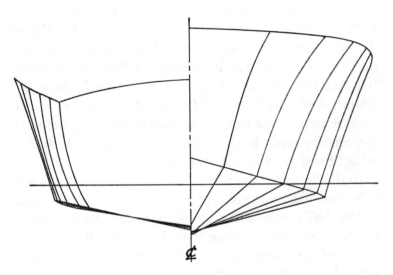

Fig. 27. Altered bottom lines of conversion design.

have to be eliminated and the warp in the after sections of the bottom would have to be eliminated, as well. Accordingly, a new set of lines was prepared, altering the bottom lines completely, eliminating both the warp in the after bottom sections almost completely and, also, the concave sections throughout the length of the bottom. Examination of Fig. 26, which shows the body plan of the original boat, and Fig. 27, which shows the body plan of the altered design, indicates graphically the changes that were made in the lines of the boat. In altering the lines, it was essential that the original chine line be retained, since any alteration of the chine would undoubtedly be very costly. Also, since only the topside sections would be adhered to, any change made in the chines would, in effect, destroy what little there was left of the boat.

In the design of the new bottom structure, careful consideration had to be given to all possible means of increasing the hull's longitudinal strength. In the original design, the boat was entirely open from Station No. 9 aft and the only deck structures existing were narrow wash boards or a planksheer, approximately 8 in. wide. Therefore, little strength was present in way of the deck and, as a result, the only way the desired longitudinal strength could be obtained would be in careful design of the bottom structure, paying particular attention to longitudinal members. Since all members of the bottom structure are considerably closer to the neutral axis of the hull girder section than the deck, scantlings of the bottom longitudinal members would have to be proportionately greater than would be the case if it were possible either to increase the existing deck structure scantlings or to add new members to the existing deck structure.

In working up the drawing of the new bottom structure, it was found that it was possible to extend the inboard engine girders from Station No. 10 all the way aft to the transom and that the sections of these two members could be fairly deep. The outboard engine girders were run as far forward and aft as possible, which amounted to a length of 14 ft. for these members. In addition, the scantlings for the new apron and keel batten were increased somewhat over the original scantlings for these members. A quick check on the new section modulus of the hull girder indicated that even these increases in scantlings for the new bottom longitudinals were not quite enough, and that either "beefing up" the new members would be required or else additional members would be necessary.

Since the original bottom planking did pant considerably in rough water, it was decided to do away with the double-planking, such as had been used in the original boat and substitute seam-batten planking. There were two very good reasons for this change. In the original boat, only the outer course of the plank skin contributed any appreciable longitudinal strength; therefore, a single plank course run longitudinally would have the effect of doubling the effective cross sectional area of the bottom planking. A further increase in the desired cross sectional area would be obtained by use of seam battens and, in addition, the seam battens would stiffen the bottom planking between frames, thereby reducing any possible tendency towards panting here. Since both the seam battens and the single course of bottom planking were farther from the neutral axis of the hull girder section than the other bottom longitudinals (with the exception of keel and apron), a very satisfying increase in the value of the new section modulus was obtained.

Many designers might have fitted hogging girders to the inside of the side frames in an attempt to stiffen up the hull longitudinally. However, it was apparent that such hogging girders would lie approximately in the same position as the neutral axis of the hull girder section at the points of maximum bending, therefore, would contribute very little to the desired longitudinal strength.

One other change which provided considerable extra strength in way of the side structure was to extend the engine box all the way from one side of the hull to the other, and to fit strong plywood bulkheads at the ends of the engine compartment. Even in twin screw models of the original boat, both engines were closed in by engine boxes, which just about covered the engines, leaving a passageway between the engines. This change in the manner of engines enclosure increased the transverse strength considerably without little increase in weight over the two engine box arrangement of the twin-engine model of the original boat.

The actual work of the conversion proceeded under the personal direction and supervision of the owner; the work being done by an exceedingly skillful and long-experienced boatbuilder. Only the finest of materials were used in the new construction. Upon completion of the work, all concerned were pleased with the results.

The new express day cruiser was weighed on a platform scale on the way to a marine railway for launching. The net weight for the completed boat with cushions and bare equipment aboard amounted to 6,220 lbs. In the water, with fuel tanks full, water tank full, ice box filled and driver only aboard, the weight of boat amounted to approximately 7,300 lbs.

The owner generously provided the writer a very comprehensive report on the performance of the express day cruiser conversion. Since the owner is an old and experienced hand in the operation of fast power boats, it is the opinion of the writer that the data given on the performance of this conversion are reasonably accurate.

On her first trials, the converted boat did 42.92 mph turning 13½" × 16" three blade wheels at 3,350 rpm. This speed check was the average speed, both with and against the current over a mile course and checked with a stop-watch. A short time later the highest priced model of the Aero-Marine speedometer was installed and at the same rpm, this instrument registered 44 mph. It was found that the boat would not plane fully at speeds below 30 mph—and this is understandable in view of the high unit planing load.

The boat's cruising water is Chesapeake Bay. On a run from Chesapeake City, Md. to Georgetown, Md., a distance of 29 nautical miles, the conversion took but 55 minutes running at 2,750 rpm—this amounts to 31.6 knots or approximately 36.4 mph. On this run, off Turkey Point, a 4 ft. chop was running, which the boat took easily without pounding at the speed noted above.

Later, when time permitted, the owner very carefully tuned both engines, then experimented with minor changes in propeller size. The best results were obtained with 13" × 18" three blade wheels, which allowed the engines to turn up the 3,450 rpm wide open. The speed over a measured mile went up to 46.31 mph with these wheels.

A graphic comparison of the performance obtained with this conversion design with that of the performance of the original design is shown in Fig. 28. Through the kindness of the Westlawn School of Yacht Design, the writer has been permitted to reproduce a part of their Approximate Speed Chart on fast open boats.

On this portion of the Westlawn Chart or Curves, the writer has spotted the performances obtained with the original design and the two performances of this conversion design. Spot (A) shows the performance of the original boat before conversion. It will be noted that on a power loading of 27.5 lbs. per hp, the speed obtainable

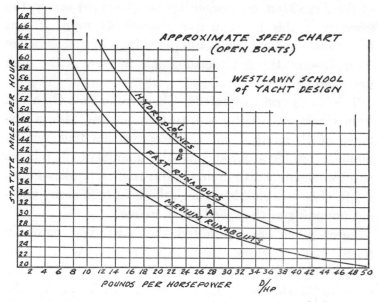

Fig. 28. Performance of original boat (A) and the same craft after conversion (B) and (C), with different propellers.

was approximately 32 mph using a 14″ × 14″ three blade propeller at 3,000 rpm and the apparent slip was 24%. The location of Spot (A) is between the performance curves for medium runabouts and fast runabouts; being closer to the fast runabout curve.

Spot (B) shows the performance of the conversion design with 13½″ × 16″ three blade wheels, which were first installed. On a power loading of 22.8 lbs per hp, the speed was 42.92 mph at 3,350 rpm; the apparent slip being 24%.

Spot (C) shows the performance obtained with the conversion design after the engines had been carefully tuned and 13″ × 18″ three blade wheels, turned at 3,450 rpm were fitted. The apparent slip dropped to 19%. As a matter of interest, the original boat when powered with a 97 bhp engine, weighed approximately 3,100 lbs with driver only aboard and would do approximately 26 mph. The unit power loading in this case was 31 lbs. per hp.

The owner reported that the handling qualities of the conversion design were satisfactory. She had been fitted with twin balanced rudders, thus would steer satisfactorily at low speeds. At planing speeds, she would bank sharply on hard turns, but it was found it was impossible to turn her over, nor did she ever show any tendency toward tripping.

The owner further reported that, to use his own words, every marine "hot rod" on Chesapeake Bay has tried to take the measure of the conversion design but without success. In one case, an expensive stock runabout with a "catalog" speed of 50 mph has been unable to take the conversion design's measure. Thus, it can be concluded that the conversion of the original runabout to an express day cruiser was reasonably successful.

It is the writer's considered opinion that it would have been highly possible to have designed an entirely new boat of similar size in an express day cruiser, using the same power, which can exceed the performance of this conversion design, obtaining full planing at a lower speed than is possible in the conversion design for the same cost figure. At the time the drawings were on the board, the writer held the opinion that the amount of the cost for this conversion would exceed the actual value of the resultant yacht. However, the writer must admit that he reckoned not with latent abilities of the owner, who was able to dispose of this conversion at the end of the yachting season without the loss of a single penny put into the job.

Much of the credit for the satisfactory results obtained with this particular conversion is due to the owner. His skill with motors and in boat handling did much in securing the maximum possible performance obtained with this conversion. Also, it was he who styled the cabin trunk and coamings, and the compact but fairly comfortable cabin arrangement; the results of his styling were quite pleasing to the eye. It might interest all of you to know that the owner mentioned in the paper happens to be an Associate Member of the s.s.c.d.

Notes on the Conversion of a Runabout   165

	Original Utility Runabout	Express Day Cruiser Conversion
Length Overall	24' 6"	24' 6"
Length Waterline	23' 5"	23' 6"
Beam	8' 0"	8' 0"
Load Displacement with driver only (no passengers)	3,800 lbs.	7,300 lbs.
Power	one Chrysler Royal Standard Model 138 bhp @ 3,000 rpm	two Chrysler Royals Special Model— total of 320 bhp @ 3,350 rpm
Propeller(s)	14" x 14" three blade	13½" x 16" three blades
Speed	32 mph	42.92 mph
Apparent Slip	24%	24%
Displ./hp	27.5 lbs./hp	22.8 lbs./hp
Approx. Area of Planing Surfaces	76.5 sq. ft.	76.5 sq. ft.
Aspect Ratio	0.308	0.308
Load Coefficient	60.4	96.4
Unit Planing Load	50 lbs./sq. ft.	96 lbs./sq. ft.

Note: Later, after careful engine tuning and replacement of 13½" x 16" wheels with 13" x 18" three blade wheels, the conversion made a speed of 46.31 mph, at 3,450 rpm, apparent slip was 19%—the total power was 326 bhp and unit power loading was 22.4 lbs./hp.

Chapter Fourteen

LET'S TALK TORQUE

By GERALD T. WHITE

OFFHAND, we may consider that it is horsepower that propels our boats.

Actually it is no such thing. It is the propeller that is doing the job, but even then horsepower is not the only factor involved even if the propeller size is correctly evaluated.

Nothing happens unless our propeller is rotated and that rotative force is not horsepower but torque, or twisting effect upon the tail shaft to which the propeller is attached.

Torque is defined as the moment which tends to twist a body about an axis of rotation. In internal combustion engineering torque may be calculated in pounds-feet (the purist objects to the use of the more usual foot-pounds) by as simple a calculation as anyone could ask for. It is:

$$\frac{5252\ P}{R}$$

when P is the brake hp and R is the rotative speed. Note that rpms are an important factor.

Let us consider two extreme cases. In one case we have 100 bhp at 300 turns and the torque in pounds-feet will be 1750, give or take a fraction. An engine developing 100 hp at 3,000 turns will have 175 pounds-feet of torque, or one-tenth as much.

It now must follow that the computation of torque is inevitably tied in with the amount of horsepower developed at a certain rotative speed. The higher the rotative speed, the lower the torque effect in spite of the fact that we must agree that the propeller has no possible use unless it is rotated and it is the torque that does the rotating. How, then, can we disregard torque and rely upon horsepower as the sole critical factor in making our power calculations?

It is no deep secret that the majority of inboard marine engines are conversions of automobile machines. In some cases the conversion has been hardly more than the amount of chicken in a 25-cent chicken pie. In other cases, considerable alterations have been made, but it would be the exception to find any major change in the torque characteristics of a specified engine used for both automobiles and boats. Slight changes, yes; major differences, no. All of this is quite in line with good engineering.

There is hardly an automobile on the market that cannot run at 90 miles an hour when everything is doing well. Likewise there are few cars on the road that have ever been driven at ninety. Designers of car engines, being aware of this, design their engines so they will have characteristics that are most suitable at the speeds attained by the average driver. The majority of these engines have their maximum torque coming in at car speeds of around 50 to 60 miles an hour. A study of a tabulation of torque for popular American car engines shows that the peak comes in at speeds averaging about 66 per cent of maximum output.

Taking one engine in particular; a Lincoln is rated at 225 hp at 4,400 rpms but her peak torque figure is given as coming in at 2,500 at which point it is 342 pounds-feet. Using the formula, it appears that the torque at 4,400 rpms must have dropped to about 270 pounds-feet even though the hp has risen considerably. We have a lot more horses but they are not turning our tail shafts and the attached propellers with anything like the same efficient conversion of the oats they ate. It should be obvious that this car was designed to operate at her best in the speed range of 55 miles an hour, more or less. No car owner can complain about this.

Those who have studied boat propulsion over the years cannot fail to realize that the present concept of the amount of horsepower installed in an average boat is fantastically higher than that which was common some years ago. In going over some old engine catalogs many records were found of 40-foot boats with less than 30 hp. This writer took a husky 45-footer to Florida and cruised at over 9 miles with an engine rated at 37 hp. It has been said over and over again that a horsepower is a horse-power. The basic calculation for hp has not changed. What, then, is the reason for the vast increase in the hp needed to propel a modern boat? Surely, we cannot believe that the hulls have greater resistance.

The answer, it seems, lies in torque; proof, if any is needed, that torque is a vital factor in our propulsion computations even if it is so seldom mentioned.

Let us look at the accompanying chart. The maximum peak of the torque curve is at about 2,500 rpms. For the sake of convenience, let us call for 200 hp which comes in at 3,200 rpms and produces 320 pounds-feet of torque. Turning back to an old catalog of heavy-duty Standard engines, we find the one-popular four-cylinder 20-24 horsepower, 5 by 6½ engine, which was rated at 20 hp at 400 rpms. This engine had one-tenth the rated horse-power of the modern machine at the 200 hp we are considering for our comparison, but her torque was 262 pounds-feet. In other words the engine most of us would call obsolete had 10 per cent of the hp of our 200 hp machine but pulled 82 per cent of her torque. This is submitted not as an argument that we should go back to 20 hp engines weighing 1,600 pounds; 80 pounds per hp; but rather to partially explain the vast importance of torque and the relative unimportance of horsepower.

If we compare on the basis of the propeller correct for the modern 200 hp at 3,200, we would call for a wheel with a diameter of 15 inches, while 20 hp at 400 would require a 32-inch wheel. If we attempted to multiply the torque of the 200 hp engine so she could use a 32-inch propeller, we would have to use a reduction gear with a

4:1 ratio but we would still be using 200 hp to turn that wheel, whereas only one-tenth of that power swung the same diameter propeller at the same rotative speed!

If we wish to be a bit cynical, we must wonder why it is that all engines, marine as well as highway, are sold with horsepower blazoned all over the ad in bold black type but that it sometimes takes an Act of Congress to worm out of a manufacturer the torque rating of his machine. This does not apply to all, or even the leading makers of boat machinery. Most of these furnish a power curve on application—some even offer it freely—from which any novice on the slide rule can calculate the torque. The better concerns even publish the torque curve, but we have yet to find any firm that talks torque in its true importance. It is still, in some quarters, a subject such as the fact that your Aunt Martha toted a shotgun to her wedding.

If we glance at the accompanying chart we cannot help but note that the horsepower curve is rising normally between 2,000 and 3,900 rpms. Above 3,900 you will note that the hp curve is beginning to reach its peak and will, if continued very far, fall over. This will be due to engine breathing characteristics, valve timing and valve gear bounce. The latter, in case it is an unfamiliar term, simply means that the valves are working so fast that they fail to seat but remain in what might be called a fluttering condition. Few engines can stand any such condition without disintegration.

But if we glance at the torque curve it seems obvious that no sane man would over-rev an engine when the torque is rapidly falling off. Carry this to an extreme and

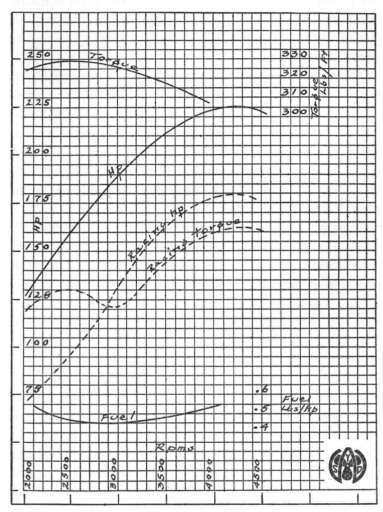

Fig. 29. Torque, horsepower and fuel curves of a popular, high-speed engine.

we would have a condition where the engine was madly spinning but delivering virtually nothing in the way of useful work. Wasting all its energy in simply moving its own parts.

Allow me to point out that these curves were prepared from sheets furnished by a leading manufacturer of marine engines of the popular type. There is nothing to be gained by mentioning the name of the engine for the curves are neither exceptionally good nor bad. The make of this engine is not quoted lest the erroneous opinion be gained that the curves are intended to condemn, or to plug, the particular make.

The peak of the torque comes in at approximately 2,500 rpms which is about 64 per cent of the peak rated speed. This is neither very low nor abnormally high and, like the engine itself, can be assumed to be a fair average. If this engine was taken over by an expert rebuilding firm, they would make alterations in the breathing and timing so that the hp curve would be extended and the torque changed so that the peak moved farther to the right.

Turning to the chart again, note the snake-like dotted curve marked for racing. This curve shows the torque developed by the well-known Coventry Climax racing engine. There is no intention to intimate that the curve is in its correct position on the sheet as far as pounds-feet are concerned. It is inserted simply to show how expert engine designers can change the torque characteristics of an engine to suit a specific job. This is an out-and-out racing car machine. For making fast starts and picking up speeds after cornering, the torque is fairly high at the low speed end of the curve. There is then a drop for the simple reason that you cannot have all you want in an internal combustion engine. Valve setting makes the hollow necessary if we are to have a fairly high torque for accelerating out of a corner.

But once this car gets rolling on a straightaway, the torque climbs so that it peaks at almost maximum rotative speed.

By coincidence, the rpms of this engine are exactly twice what the chart shows so that the peak of its torque comes in at nearly 9,000 turns. That any such machine is suitable only for racing is obvious. If used for normal services, the low point in the torque would occur at just about highway speeds. It is of further interest to know that the peak of this torque curve also comes at the peak of the hp curve, which is also shown dotted. Compare these two dotted curves for shape with the solid lines for the normal engine torque and horsepower curves.

Turning back to our normal engine again we find the important point is that for maximum twisting force the non-racing engine should be run at about 2,500 rpms where the power output would be 160 hp. It is seldom that economical operation does not closely check with torque efficiency. For that reason the fuel consumption curve of the same engine has been included on the curve sheet. Fuel consumption is based on pounds per brake hp and you will note that the curve is dish-shaped with its peak at about 2,000 at one end and 4,000 at the other. The low point of the curve is at 2,900 at which point the torque curve has dropped but slightly, being only about 9 pounds-feet less than at its peak. If we are to combine maximum fuel-economy per hp with maximum torque, it is obvious that the engine should be run somewhere between 2,500 and 2,900—2700 being the mean. Note that the shape of the torque curve is the opposite to that of the fuel curve. One is crowned, the other dished.

The weight of gasoline varies slightly depending upon its chemistry but is generally accepted at 6 pounds per gallon. Our average fuel consumption is so close to .5 pounds that we can accept that as a good standard providing we realize that power curves are prepared in the testing laboratory where every condition is ideal.

If we translate that into terms of our sample engine running at the best average for both torque and fuel consumption—that is 2,700—we would find that the hp at that rotative speed divided by 11.8 will give us the gallons per hour used in the test room. This, if we accept the fact that an engine buried under hatches and adjusted once a season must fall short of the test room results, does not come too far from the rule of thumb that dividing the hp by 10 will give the service consumption in gallons an hour, whereas 12 would be the divisor for the test bench.

There is a general fallacy that operating revs can be varied through a great range just as they are in cars. The owner, wishing to save gasoline, feels certain that all he has to do is to close the throttle, using full rotative speeds only when he wants to get somewhere in a hurry.

Previous s.s.c.d. papers have pointed out that any such sweet dream simply does not work. The propeller size that is correct for, say, 3,000 rpms is a complete bust if run at 1,500. Gasoline is saved but the boat speed per gallon of fuel is knocked in the head. If we are to take advantage of maximum torque, or turning moment on our propellers, we must specify that our power plants be operated constantly at the most efficient speed obtained from the curve sheets with the exception that, in crowded waters, or when making a landing, the owner must slow down, using common sense but with the understanding that every minute he runs more slowly his efficiency is falling off; that being his way of paying for safe boat handling.

Chapter Fifteen

SCANTLING RULES

From the Notebook of a Member of the s.s.c.d.

THESE are the scantling rules that were proposed by one of our late leading yacht builders and based on his broad experience in building many types of vessels during his lifetime. These rules are in active use in a number of large yacht designing offices.

GENERAL CLAUSES

$\sqrt[3]{D}$ (with the yacht in load condition) expressed in cubic feet is the basis upon which scantlings are calculated.

Where any deviation from the scantlings or the usual method of construction is proposed, hull should be of equal weight and equal strength to that specified in the following tables.

The materials specified are those which are deemed most suitable in each instance. The scantlings are based

176

upon their use. Should it be desired to substitute other kinds of materials, they should be of equal weight and strength but no reduction in size may be taken for heavier materials than those specified.

In determining relative weights and strengths of wood, the tables in *U.S. Department of Agriculture Misc. Publication No. 46* shall be the authority. For woods not covered in this publication, any standard table may be used.

Where Mahogany is specified, it should weigh not less than 32 pounds per cubic foot.

All fastenings not specified in the tables should be adequate for their purpose and, in general, to provide maximum strength obtainable at the joining of two members.

All deck openings should be adequately framed in.

There should be proper breast hooks, transom knees, mast partners and mast steps.

Keel

Material: White Oak, Teak, or Mahogany.
Molding: Not less than $\sqrt[3]{D}$ multiplied by .7.
Siding: Not less than double the molding at the widest part of the keel.

Stem

Material: White Oak, Teak, or Mahogany.
Siding: At head not less than four times the thickness of the planking. Below head the siding of stem and bow timber shall be gradually increased to siding of keel to provide proper back rabbet.
Molding: Not less than siding.

STERNPOST

Material: White Oak, Teak, or Mahogany.
Molding: Not less than siding.
Siding: Not less than four times thickness of plank.

HORN TIMBER

Material: White Oak, Teak, or Mahogany.
Molding: Not less than twice the thickness of plank.
Siding: Not less than twice the molding.

FRAMES

Material: White Oak, steam-bent.
Sectional Area: At heel in accordance with table sizes.
May be straight-tapered to head to not less than 75
per cent of the heel area.

Where untapered frame is used, rule size shall be
maintained for three-quarters of L.W.L. length. Fore
and aft of the three-quarters length the area may be
gradually reduced to the ends of the yacht where it
may be 15 per cent less than amidships.

Where tapered frame is used, the rule shall be
applied to the longest frame in the yacht, establishing thereby a standard taper for all other frames.
The head size of the longest frame shall be maintained throughout yacht and the established taper
applied therefrom, to the heel, thereby decreasing
the areas at the heel as the frames grow shorter fore
and aft of the longest frame.

Molding: Optional. Table dimensions are recommended.
In no case less than is required to entirely bury the
plank fastenings of the length specified for screws.

Siding: Optional. Table dimensions recommended.
Spacing: To be in accordance with table.

Where severe bends are encountered making it impractical to use a solid frame, it is recommended that the frame be split, in a fore and aft direction, from the end to just beyond the point of extreme bend, or a double frame may be used, one member bent inside the other. In both instances, plank fastenings should extend through outer member well into inner member and the two be drawn tightly together.

If sawn frames are to be used, they shall be double, with the members adequately bolted or riveted together. Sectional Area: 50 per cent heavier than the table size of frames.

BELT FRAMES

Material: White Oak, steam-bent.
Molding: Three-quarters that of frames.
Siding: Equal to frames.

Belt frames are to be applied to yachts which are ceiled and there must be at least four on each side. They shall be applied after ceiling is installed.

In the case of single-masted vessels and yawls, one set of belt frames is to be located immediately forward and one immediately aft of main mast, and are to be kneed to heavy partner deck beams.

Belt frames should be used whenever possible, but, should they interfere with any unusual condition inside the yacht, may be omitted, provided the regular frame at that location is doubled in sectional area or two frames of rule size placed alongside each other and bolted or riveted together. Yachts which are not ceiled are to be fitted with heavy frames having a sectional area of one and three-quarter times the area of main frames and located in a like manner to belt frames of ceiled yachts.

In the case of two-masted schooners or ketches, one set of belt frames are to be located immediately forward and one immediately aft of each mast and are to be kneed to heavier partner deck beams.

In the case of three-masted yachts, there shall be six pair belt frames, one set located immediately forward and one immediately aft of each mast which are to be kneed to heavy partner deck beams.

PLANKING

Material: Teak, Mahogany, L.L. Yellow Pine and Douglas Fir.

Thickness: In accordance with table.

Butts to be shifted so that no two butts shall come on same frame or in same frame space except there be three clear plank between and in no adjacent plank be nearer than three frame spaces.

If Teak is used, thickness may be reduced ten per cent.

CEILING

Material: L.L. Yellow Pine, Douglas Fir or Spruce.

Thickness: Forty per cent of the table thickness of outside planking. No reduction allowed where Teak planking is used.

Ceiling shall be fitted in all yachts having a D of over ten, and shall extend for at least the waterline length of the vessel and from cabin sole to underside of clamp

Bilge Stringers

Material: L.L. Yellow Pine or Douglas Fir.

Sectional Area: Equal to three times the table area of frames for three-quarters of L.W.L. length.

Bilge stringers shall be used in all yachts which are not ceiled. There shall be one on each side to extend from stem to stern wherever possible, and may be straight-tapered to ends to not less than 50 per cent of the area amidships.

Clamp and Shelf

Material: L.L. Yellow Pine or Douglas Fir.

Sectional Area: Three and one-half times the table area of frames for three-quarters of the waterline length.

They shall extend the full length of the yacht but may be straight-tapered to the ends to not less than 50 per cent of the area amidships.

A single clamp or a clamp and shelf of required area may be used.

Deck Beams

Material: Oak, Chestnut, Douglas Fir, L.L. Yellow Pine, Teak, Mahogany and Ash.

Sectional Area: At center line of boat in accordance with table and may be reduced at ends to 75 per cent of the sectional area at center.

Spacing: Same as table for frames.

Molding: Optional. May be reduced at ends to 75 per cent of the molding at center.

Siding: Optional, but to be not more than 65 per cent of the molding at center.

There shall be partner beams and hatch beams whose siding shall be one and three-quarters times the siding of the main beams.

Half beams and beams beyond the ends of the L.W.L. may be reduced to 75 per cent of the area of the main beams.

DECKING

Material: White Pine, Cedar, Spruce, Cypress or Douglas Fir.

Thickness: Same as outside planking.

If Teak is used, the thickness may be reduced ten per cent. If covered with canvas, thickness may be reduced one-eighth of an inch.

FLOORS

Material: White Oak, Teak, Mahogany.

Spacing: One to each pair of frames.

Siding: Not less than frame.

Molding: To be sufficient to allow at least four fastenings to heels of frames, whose spacing shall be not less than one and one-half times siding of floor, but in no case shall the sectional area over the keel be less than twice the sectional area of frames.

In way of lead keel, siding of floors taking keel bolts shall be increased to regular siding, plus the diameter of the keel bolt. Molding to be same as regular floors.

There shall be no concave on top of any floor to show up cross-grains at ends.

In any yacht where it is necessary to use the space occupied by wooden floors to install tanks or to meet any special conditions, metal floors may be used of approved design and of equal weight and strength to the wooden floors.

HULL STRAPS

Material: Bronze of not less than sixty thousand pounds per square inch of tensile strength.

Width: Twice the planking thickness.

Thickness: One-tenth the plank thickness. (Other dimensions may be used but shall produce an equal cross-sectional area.)

There shall be two diagonal straps on each side at each mast extending from under side of deck to keel between outside of frame and inside of the planking.

Straps shall be fastened at each crossing of frame and between frames to the planking.

DECK STRAPS

Material: Same as hull straps.

Width: Same as hull straps.

Thickness: Same as hull straps.

Yachts to be fitted with two diagonal straps at each mast extending from gunwale to gunwale between top of deck beam and under side of deck and not cut by deck openings.

To be fastened at each beam crossing and between beams into deck.

HANGING KNEES

Material: Wood, cast bronze, steel or bronze plate flanged to frames or deck beams.
Length of Arms: 1.75 times table frame spacing.

PLANK FASTENINGS

Material: Wood screws of non-corrosive metal.
Length: Twice the plank thickness from heel to turn of bilge; from turn of bilge to head may be shortened to suit molding frame.

Size: Plank Thickness	Gauge
⅝″	#9
¾″	10
⅞″	12
1″	14
1⅛″	16
1¼″	18
1½″	20
1¾″	22
2″	24
2¼″	26
2½″	28

Should other type of fastening be used, such as bolts, rivets or drift fastenings, they shall be of equal cross-sectional area to the table for wood screws and of suitable length.

LEAD KEEL BOLTS

Material: Bronze, having a tensile strength of not less than 60,000 pounds per square inch.

The number and size to be sufficient to give not less than one square inch of sectional area of bolt for 1,500 pounds of outside ballast.

It has been the writer's observation that the backbones or keel framing of a large percentage of many published designs are much too heavy for normal use, especially in these days when large sound and well-seasoned timbers are difficult to obtain. Of course if one is designing a boat for Arctic or ice conditions they are needed.

However, the backbone of some normal designs shown in profile would be so oversize if sided as required that it becomes a puzzle that the boat will ever float anywhere near her designed waterline. Consequently, the following notes to this and other items should merit your attention.

KEEL: Since the garboard plank and floor timbers are often the only tie between the frame and keel member and especially where the frames are cut for limbers, it becomes desirable that the garboard plank is also fastened to the keel. Also in many cases the hood ends of the planking also land on the keel. Hence it becomes desirable that a minimum back rabbet be maintained of 1¾ to 2 T where T is the plank thickness.

LIMBERS: These should be double throughout except where width permits only single limber. All limbers should be of ample size to facilitate cleaning, smallest dimension never less than ⅝″, area of limbers should increase progressively from ends as they approach the low point of the bilge. Each individual should be slightly tapered so that it is larger on the side toward the low point of the bilge. Double chains should be fitted throughout to facilitate cleaning the limbers. Pockets which are difficult to clean should be eliminated by making the keel structure the full width to the inside of the planking where possible.

Where this is not possible, as at the extreme forward end of the horn timber, the limber should be tapered in a way from the planking to avoid the extremely acute angle which creates a space that is impractical to keep clean and to adequately drain. A minimum of unavoidable small pockets may be filled with Minnesota Mining or Woolsey's calking compound but it is still best to shape the wooden members so that there are as few possible small corners. No bitumastic compound that melts in warm weather should be used since it is conceivable that a boat laid up for a season ashore will open up and compound will flow into the seams and remain there so that the planking will never fully swell shut again and a minor leak will come into existence that no amount of calking can overcome. It is also important that all butt blocks, transom frame, etc. should be worked out so there are no corners which will catch shavings, dirt or water.

STEM MOLDING AND SIDING: Normally the molding and siding of the stem at the head should not be less than that required by the scantling rules which in the case of these rules should be $4T$, where T is the planking thickness. Occasionally, this may be insufficient especially for either a very sharp deck outline or a very full deck line at the stem. In the former case the molding will be insufficient and in the latter the siding will be insufficient. In all cases this should be carefully checked by the procedure as outlined below:

Sections should be taken normal to the profile throughout the forebody at the rabbet line in the manner as outlined in any treatise on laying down. However, sections at the ends of waterlines or the stations seldom give a true picture of the rabbet.

On each true section of the rabbet, the backbone should be laid out so that the distance between the port and starboard planking should never be less han $2T$ minimum to permit necessary through fastenings, and there should be a back rabbet of not less than 1¾ to $2T$. Furthermore, so that there is sufficient wood for fastening the hood ends of the planking, there should be a minimum of 1½T thickness of keel backbone measured normal to the inner surface at a point ¾T inboard of the outer edge of the back rabbet.

Consequently, in some cases, depending on the angle the planking makes with the centerline of the ship, an increased molding or siding may become necessary as we've already noted.

After sufficient sections of this type have been drawn, a minimum molding that gives a 1¾ to $2T$ back rabbet and as further noted above can now be drawn in. This is the minimum molding and has disregarded all intermediate stem knees and scarphs which can now be laid out so that this requirement is still maintained.

Incidentally, there is an over tendency to avoid feather edges by making the nibs of scarphs too deep. Actually 1″ maximum is sufficient especially if there is ample siding and the through fastenings are well distributed. Also it is impossible to avoid feather edges in a transverse direction.

HORN TIMBER: The horn timber is laid out in a similar manner to the stem and forward deadwood. Actually, most boats are quite flat and the horn timber will be molded about $3T$ and siding as little as 3½ to $6T$ exclusive of siding required for rudder stock or propeller shaft.

METHOD TO REVISE SCANTLINGS TO SUIT REVISED FRAME SPACING

Often it becomes desirable to use a frame spacing other than that required by the rules and in that case the principal scantlings should be modified accordingly as noted below by Factor A which is the square root of the frame spacing desired divided by the frame spacing required or

$$\text{Factor } A = \sqrt{\frac{\text{Frame Spacing Desired}}{\text{Frame Spacing by Rule}}}$$

The thickness of Planking and siding of Floors are to be modified by Factor A.

The sectional area of the Frame is to be modified by Factor A.

The total sectional area of the Clamp and a continuous Shelf is to be modified by Factor A. The sectional area of the clamp is to be slightly larger than the sectional area of the shelf.

Likewise the siding of Deck Beams, thickness of the Decking, sectional area of the Belt Frames, Partners, etc. are to be multiplied by Factor A.

The sectional area of the Bilge Stringers should be modified by Factor A, except the thickness of the bilge stringers should be equal to the final planking thickness and consists of sufficient strakes to give the required total sectional area.

Molding and siding of other principal scantlings not specifically noted above shall be as required by the scantling rules.

Incidentally when possible a frame spacing of 10" center to center has worked out to be very satisfactory in many cases as it is possible to land the bulkheads on frames and still have the desired arrangement plan.

HANGING KNEES: It has become quite common practice to arrange the construction plan so that the plywood bulkheads would land on the side of the frames and deck beams, eliminating hanging knees except when impractical, such as mast partners in the middle of a cabin where hanging knees are required but bulkheads would not be possible.

Also the bulkheads for this purpose are often 50 per cent thicker than those normally required for joiner-work and are through bolted to the frames and beams in addition to being attached to the bilge stringers by clips. Also, these are quite often glued to avoid nuisance squeaking and working of the bulkheads.

LODGING KNEES AND DECK STRAPPING: Lodging knees and deck strapping are not necessary when using a plywood deck but are absolutely necessary on a laid deck. However, some consideration should always be made when the time comes to replace a canvas deck that it will not require the use of quarter round battens, etc., or the removal of even the cabin trunk, hatches, and bulwarks simply to replace a canvas deck. It is much better that this be given consideration in the initial stages of the design.

MAST STEPS: In these days of tall rigs, the compression load on a sloop or yawl mainmast may easily equal the displacement and it is extremely vital that the mast step should distribute this load over ample area. This should be at least 6-8 frame spaces. Also, for this reason it is very desirable that there is no scarph in the keel backbone under the mast step or at the forward end of the ballast keel, which will only open up in time and become an endless source of leaks after a few years of continued sailing. Consequently, in a small cruising boat, it becomes quite a problem to design a suitable mast step that will have sufficient strength but which will not unduly interfere with the cabin layout.

In conclusion, I have attempted to discuss briefly a few random notes to clarify the use of the scantling rules for those unusual cases and cover items that were mentioned in my informal talk that was given last year when I presented some scantling rules to the Society.

BASIC SCANTLING TABLE FOR SIZE AND SPACING
OF FRAMES, DECK BEAMS AND PLANKING

EDITOR'S NOTE: These scantling tables specifically apply to keel-type, round-bottom, sailing craft with frames having the same dimensions both sided and molded. See text matter.

$\sqrt{D}$ cu. ft.	Frame Area (sq. in.)	Frames Sided and Molded	Frame Spacing	Plank thickness	Deck Beam Area (sq. in.)	$\sqrt{D}$ cu. ft.	Frame Area (sq. in)	Frames Sided and Molded	Frame Spacing	Plank thickness	Deck Beam Area (sq. in.)
4.0	.65	.81	6.03	.56	.75	10.4	8.70	2.95	14.20	1.66	7.05
4.2	.75	.87	6.30	.59	.88	10.6	9.10	3.02	14.44	1.70	7.31
4.4	.86	.93	6.58	.62	1.03	10.8	9.50	3.09	14.68	1.73	7.58
4.6	1.00	1.00	6.84	.66	1.18	11.0	9.92	3.15	14.92	1.76	7.85
4.8	1.13	1.07	7.12	.69	1.33	11.2	10.36	3.22	15.16	1.80	8.12
5.0	1.28	1.13	7.38	.72	1.49	11.4	10.80	3.29	15.40	1.83	8.41
5.2	1.43	1.20	7.64	.75	1.65	11.6	11.29	3.36	15.63	1.86	8.70
5.4	1.60	1.27	7.91	.79	1.81	11.8	11.78	3.44	15.88	1.90	9.00
5.6	1.80	1.34	8.18	.82	1.98	12.0	12.30	3.51	16.12	1.93	9.30
5.8	1.98	1.41	8.44	.86	2.15	12.2	12.80	3.58	16.35	1.96	9.60
6.0	2.20	1.48	8.70	.90	2.33	12.4	13.31	3.65	16.60	1.99	9.91
6.2	2.40	1.55	8.97	.93	2.50	12.6	13.87	3.73	16.83	2.02	10.22
6.4	2.61	1.62	9.22	.96	2.67	12.8	14.42	3.80	17.07	2.05	10.53
6.6	2.83	1.69	9.49	1.00	2.85	13.0	15.00	3.88	17.31	2.09	10.84
6.8	3.10	1.76	9.73	1.04	3.03	13.2	15.55	3.95	17.55	2.12	11.16
7.0	3.34	1.86	10.00	1.08	3.22	13.4	16.14	4.02	17.80	2.15	11.49
7.2	3.59	1.90	10.25	1.12	3.42	13.6	16.74	4.09	18.03	2.18	11.84
7.4	3.84	1.96	10.50	1.15	3.62	13.8	17.33	4.16	18.28	2.22	12.16
7.6	4.12	2.03	10.75	1.18	3.82	14.0	17.95	4.24	18.50	2.25	12.60
7.8	4.40	2.10	11.00	1.22	4.02	14.2	18.60	4.32	18.75	2.28	12.84
8.0	4.70	2.17	11.25	1.25	4.22	14.4	19.20	4.39	19.00	2.31	13.18
8.2	5.00	2.24	11.50	1.29	4.43	14.6	19.87	4.46	19.22	2.34	13.52
8.4	5.30	2.30	11.75	1.32	4.64	14.8	20.50	4.53	19.45	2.37	13.86
8.6	5.60	2.34	12.00	1.36	4.86	15.0	21.12	4.60	19.70	2.40	14.21
8.8	5.90	2.43	12.25	1.40	5.09	15.2	21.80	4.67	19.95	2.43	14.58
9.0	6.23	2.50	12.50	1.43	5.32	15.4	22.50	4.75	20.18	2.46	14.95
9.2	6.53	2.56	12.75	1.46	5.55	15.6	23.17	4.82	20.42	2.50	15.31
9.4	6.89	2.63	13.00	1.50	5.78	15.8	23.90	4.89	20.65	2.53	15.68
9.6	7.22	2.69	13.23	1.53	6.02	16.0	24.60	4.96	20.88	2.55	16.05
9.8	7.58	2.76	13.47	1.56	6.27	16.2	25.30	5.03	21.12	2.58	16.43
10.0	7.92	2.82	13.72	1.60	6.53	16.4	26.00	5.10	21.36	2.60	16.80
10.2	8.30	2.88	13.96	1.63	6.79						

Chapter Sixteen

ALUMINUM ALLOYS IN SMALL CRAFT DESIGN AND CONSTRUCTION

By THOMAS E. COLVIN

THE use of aluminum alloys in small craft design and construction is an exhaustive topic, but it is hoped that the information presented here will be of some value to those contemplating the use of aluminum in small craft design. The primary purpose of this paper is to give a little more than the basic information necessary to be incorporated in the plans of an aluminum vessel and enough of the various considerations and procedures that are used in aluminum construction. Perhaps this will answer some of the more pertinent questions that usually arise when one enters into this medium, such as: How is aluminum welded? How is it riveted? etc.

When thinking of aluminum, it is amazing when one learns that it comprises over 1/12th of the earth's crust. Aluminum is twice as plentiful as iron, although it is never found in a free form such as gold, silver or some of the richer copper ores. It is obtained from red clays which contain high portions of alumina which is the aluminum oxide. The foods we eat and some of our precious stones, such as the sapphire, turquoise, topaz, ruby and garnet are compounds of aluminum.

The chemical process involved in extracting aluminum is so costly that only ores with a high alumina content are used; such ores are called bauxite. The principal producing areas are France, the Dutch Guianas, West Hungary, Dalmatia, and the middle southern states. It is mined in a similar fashion to iron or coal in that the mining process may be strip, open pit, or underground; but here its similarity to the other metal ends.

HISTORICAL BACKGROUND

Aluminum was first discovered in 1825 by Hans Christian Oersted who was a professor of physics at the University of Copenhagen, Denmark. His first product was apparently a metallic aluminum. A couple of years later, Frederick Woehler, a German scientist produced aluminum in the form of a gray powder, and in 1845 was able to form particles of the powder into a solid. These particles were very small, being approximately the size of a pinhead. Woehler also discovered that it was easy to shape, to melt, and was very stable in air.

In 1852, just a little over 100 years ago, aluminum sold for $545 a pound, which was higher and more precious than gold or silver. In 1854, the French scientist, Henri Claire Deville, and the German professor, Robert Von Bunsen, in separate discoveries, learned to isolate aluminum by using sodium instead of potassium, thus what had formerly been small particles of aluminum were now large chunks of aluminum.

In 1886, the greatest stride in aluminum was made by two men—one an American and the other a Frenchman —coincidentally, both were the same age. Charles Martin Hall and Paul T. Heroult both applied for patents in the same year, each securing patents in his own country. Their discovery was that metallic aluminum could be produced by dissolving alumina in molten cryolite at about 1,800° F., obtaining about 22 per cent alumina, and then passing an electric current through the solution. As a result, the price of aluminum dropped in 7 years from $11.33 to 57 cents a pound. By 1900, aluminum was 23 cents a pound, and in 1942, 14 cents a pound, and today it is back to approximately 50 cents a pound in shapes and plates.

The Hall and Heroult process is called the electrolytic reduction process. Electrolytic reduction basically is the breaking down of alumina into aluminum and oxygen. The oxygen combines with carbon at the anodes and passes off as carbon dioxide gas. Since aluminum melts at about 1,200° F. and cryolite at about 1,800° F. the action is continuous. It takes about 20,000 kilowatt hours to produce a ton of aluminum. It takes approximately four tons of bauxite to make two tons of alumina which result in one ton of metallic aluminum. In this process about 1,500 pounds of carbon electrodes are consumed as well.

This first molting is poured into what is called primary aluminum pig and when fluxed and skimmed becomes a primary aluminum ingot. Aluminum sheets are rolled above ⅛″ by heat and below ⅛″ cold. Rods, bars and wire are drawn and shapes are made similarly to scale by the extrusion process. Aluminum weighs about ⅓ as much as copper, steel or brass. Aluminum does not rust. An oxide which forms on the outer surface, unlike rust in iron, protects the basic metal; whereas in iron, the basic metal is allowed to rust continuously. Pure aluminum in itself is rather soft and weak and has a yield strength of approximately 5,000 lbs. Yet, when it is alloyed, one of the aluminums has a 71,000 lb. yield strength. Aluminum is alloyed with such elements as manganese, magnesium, copper, zinc, etc.

GENERAL CONSIDERATIONS

For equal strength, aluminum weighs ⅓ as much as steel. However, to have equal rigidity, it weighs about ½ as much as steel. The average weight-saving, when aluminum is used as compared to steel, will be between 38-40 per cent, since in small craft there are very few instances where the strength of the shell is more than just lightly considered, the primary consideration being to eliminate washboarding.

Strength calculations should be made for every new type of aluminum hull until such time as the designer has sufficient data to construct a series of curves which will enable him to pick out the component parts of a hull. Even then, a series of rough calculations are desirable to ensure that adequate strength is present and that various members are not too strong for adjacent stiffening and framing. Longitudinal framing is especially suited to aluminum construction.

First cost, when it is a deciding factor, will not permit the use of aluminum in preference to steel. However, when considering the cost over a period of ten years plus the greater speed with which aluminum may be worked, the comparisons between the two are very close. A properly equipped building yard will further increase the speed of production in aluminum over that of steel. In the final analysis of the cost of building an aluminum hull versus a steel hull, the material value of the metal will be about 4 to 5 times that of steel. The reduction in displacement due to the use of lighter metals will be a saving that can be incorporated into comparative prices.

DESIGN CONSIDERATIONS

In designing with aluminum, there are a great many factors to consider, many of which are covered elsewhere in this paper. The concept of design in aluminum is akin to both metal and wood-to-metal in that it is a metal and must be treated as one, and to wood, in that it can be shaped to almost any conceivable form. In fact, by extruding and/or forging, it can be shaped into a greater variety of forms than wood can by gluing or by any other known method at present. The weight factor in aluminum is often such that it is of primary importance, especially in trailered boats, life boats, or those that are to be taken out of the water either by hoists or on a floating dock. Reduction in weight over molded plywood and wood lends itself to aluminum.

Figure A (Fig. 30) indicates an extrusion suitable for a gunwale bar on a small aluminum sloop where the shell and decks are to be of riveted construction. It is superior in appearance to the gunwale bars which are lapped over the side and deck plating. Its main disadvantage is that care must be exercised in the cutting of plates so as to en-

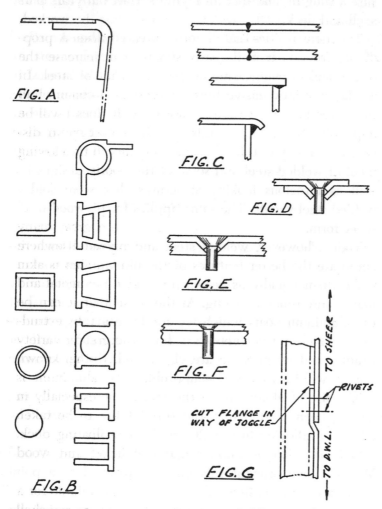

FIG. A

FIG. C

FIG. D

FIG. E

FIG. F

FIG. B

CUT FLANGE IN
WAY OF JOGGLE

RIVETS

TO SHEER

TO D.W.L.

FIG. G

Fig. 30. Aluminum extrusions; welding and riveting methods.

sure a snug fit, and that all faying surfaces are fair to the shell and deck.

The monstrosities that are often created when a method of construction is in its early stages of development are due to lack of engineering knowledge or in the interest of a relatively inexpensive finished product. Consumerwise, the latter may be desirable; however, it does create an impression that all such hulls must have that appearance. One needs only to think back a few years to the development of welded steel and some of the poorly designed as well as atrocious looking structures that were sold as welded steel yachts. The same applies for plywood in the sheet form.

Today, however, welded steel and plywood boats incorporate the better features of the old wooden boats to make them equally as seaworthy and often structurally many more times as strong. At the present time, many of the aluminum boats which we see have many protuberances which are not necessary for structural strength or beauty, and when these are eliminated, the appearance quality will be improved many-fold.

The use of aluminum in the marine field is not new, having been used before the turn of the century. The advent of alloying in the '20's and especially the perfection in erection techniques and welding during World War II, have brought this material forward to a point where its use is feasible.

The use of aluminum in cruising boats that are 100 per cent power driven offers no obstacles in regard to weight other than that the center of gravity of the hull is usually much lower than when steel or wood is used.

In cruising sailing boats of all sizes, aluminum will

produce a much lighter hull than other materials, and, at the same time, because of its lightness will produce a reduction in displacement with a corresponding reduction in sail area, if so desired.

Referring to the Cruising Club of America Rule where sail area is in direct proportion to the displacement of the vessel, it is found, in racing craft, that all other factors being the same, especially the rated length (the combination of load waterline and 4 per cent waterline length), ballast to displacement, measured beam, draft, freeboard, propeller location and type, etc., because of aluminum's light weight, a corresponding reduction in displacement is necessary which causes a reduction in sail area as well as a reduction in the total amount of ballast. It will be seen immediately that aluminum would enter favorably into the light displacement type of hull. Whether or not the reduction in sail area, displacement and ballast are desirable rests with the individual designer.

It is well to note that there are boats of either extreme winning long distance races today—*Hoot Mon* being an example of one extreme, and *Finisterre* an example of the other. Each designer has his own personal preference and theory as to which is best. Certainly a reduction in displacement can be a reduction in wetted surface which, in turn, directly affects the speed of a hull. The reduction in sail area is a loss of power; however, by adapting the rig and its aspect ratio to a smaller total rated area, the difference in actual sail area is never noticed. It is often found desirable to increase the weight of the aluminum shape to decrease the cost even though the strength of the lighter shape were sufficient.

When contemplating an aluminum vessel, therefore, it

is desirable that the designer and the owner weigh the advantages and disadvantages as well as ultimate cost, and that preliminary plans be drawn rather fluid to be finalized when a comparative cost analysis can be made of various aluminum shapes, since there is a decided difference between the cost of any two shapes. An expanded shell and shell framing drawing should be supplied along with the other customary drawings comprising the total design.

EXTRUSIONS, FORGINGS, PIPES, TANKS, ETC.

Aluminum alloys are such that the possibilities of extrusions or forgings or of combinations of both should always be explored. Since the dies necessary for this work are relatively inexpensive, the possibilities of extrusions are limitless. In the mass production or in quantity production of any item, extrusions and forging should be investigated since great savings in overall cost are possible. Figure B (Fig. 30) shows several extrusions which are possible. Detailed drawings sent to the aluminum manufacturer will be processed by them and returned showing the tolerances which they must allow in extrusion.

In comparison with other metals, aluminum is third in malleability, fifth in ductility, and exceeded only by silver and copper in electrical conductivity.

Aluminum tubes are readily bent depending, of course, on the thickness of the walls and bendability of the material which is affected by its ductility and strength. Having ductility and little strength, elongation is the result of bending; whereas, strength without ductility will cause fracture in the bend. For very hard bends, the softer tempers of aluminum are best. Aluminum tubing, in general, can be welded gas-tight and air-tight, which makes it an excellent material for hydraulic lines, gas lines or oil lines, water lines, etc. It is also a good material for railings and stanchions.

The use of aluminum with a dissimilar metal in connection of salt water lines will create corrosion almost immediately due to galvanic action. If this must be done, the use of a bituminous base paint will often be sufficient as a barrier between the two metals.

The use of aluminum for tanks to hold inflammable liquids offers a safety feature in that no spark is created by aluminum in association with other metals. Suitable joints for welding of gas tanks, water tanks, etc. are indicated in Figure C (Fig. 30). A 5-foot static head should be a minimum requirement for any tank containing liquids in marine use.

Aluminum can be used for lighting fixtures, as well as hardware such as latches, doorknobs, etc., which are offered in many styles and finishes and can be integrated into almost any decoration scheme.

RIVETING

Of all the methods of fastening aluminum, and there are hundreds, riveting is probably the most common. There are several alloys suitable for marine use of which rivets are made. In the fastening of the 52 and 61 alloy groups, the rivets of the 61-S alloy are probably the best. Occasionally steel rivets are used with aluminum; however, it is necessary to insulate the steel from the aluminum to eliminate galvanic action. It is always best to have a completely homogeneous structure. The 61-S rivets are usually supplied in the T-6 temper which is solution heat-treated and aged and can be stored with no change in its properties. This rivet is also available in the T-4 temper for hot driving, which must be accomplished at about 990° to 1050° F. The rivets age to full strength at room temperature in 10 to 14 days. The properties, when driven hot, are not affected. The rivet joints in aluminum are similar to those of steel—either butt or lap—and have the same arrangement, viz., single, double or treble riveted, etc., either parallel or chain.

Riveted joint failures are, of course, due to shear of the rivet, tension in the plate or cover plates, shearing or tearing of the plate between rivet holes and the edge of the plate, or by crushing of the rivet or of the plate at the edge of the hole. It is seldom that a joint is ever subject to pure tension so that other failures, which may and often do occur, are the popping of the heads, the heads pulling through the sheet, etc.; however, these failures can be controlled by correct proportioning of the riveted joints and proper driving of the rivets.

The basic rule for selecting rivets is: the diameter of any rivet used should never be smaller than the thickness of the thinnest plate, nor more than three times the thickness of the thinnest plate. It is better to have a rivet too long for driving than one too short, since there is little chance of damaging plates with long rivets. As in steel, rivet holes should be punched or drilled and reamed. It is usual to call for this in the specifications.

A preferred method, of course is sub-punching or sub-drilling and reaming. Punched plates will have a burr and will be liable to have small cracks radiating from the punch. Such cracks will reduce the strength of the joint. The minimum pitch to rivets should not be less than

three times the diameter of the rivet and not greater than
24 times the thickness of the thinnest plate. Edge distance
should be 1½ times the diameter of the hole. To calculate
the shear strength, tensile strength and bearing strength
of rivets, the formulas are:

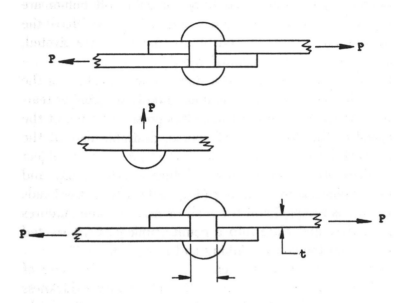

$P/A = S$ (Shear)

$P/A = T$ (Tension)

$P/td = B$ (Bearing)

A = Area; P = Pull; S = Shear; T = Tension; B =
    Bearing; t = thickness of plate; d = diameter of
    the rivet.

Fatigue failures are most common in the plate, not in
the rivet, and shear failures in the rivet itself are very
rare. Punching makes for the lowest endurance limit; a
well-drilled hole is next; and sub-punching or sub-drilling

and reaming provides the best endurance. Fatigue strength tends to increase with the number of rows of rivets. Riveted joints in double shear have better fatigue strength than in single shear. Cold-driven steel rivets are better in fatigue than hot-driven steel rivets; however, in aluminum, the difference between cold and hot-driven rivets is negligible. Fatigue strength increases with size of the rivet. Butt-riveted joints have greater fatigue strength than lap joints, and the double-spliced plate has a better fatigue joint than a single-spliced plate.

In drilling aluminum, pneumatic tools are always to be preferred to electric tools since it is possible to control the speed of the drill. It is, of course, desirable to have all riveting flush in small craft.

There are several methods of flush riveting aluminum. One method is by dimpling (Figure D, Fig. 30) wherein the die is recessed and the mall or driving hammer sinks both rivet and plate into a countersunk joint where the rivet does the countersinking and finishes flush. This can be used on very thin sheets.

Another method of flush riveting (Figure E, Fig. 30) is by countersinking the inner plate and driving rivets and the thinner plate into the countersink.

The third method of flush riveting (Figure F, Fig. 30) is one that is most adaptable to small craft in that only the outer plate is countersunk, the rivets being driven flush as in the case of steel.

Round head is to be preferred over the many other types of available heads, since it is the easiest to maintain. Hammerhead speeds should be between 900 and 2,500 blows per minute. The fast hammers, while suitable for the aircraft industry, are not generally suitable in marine work.

As shown in Figure G, Fig. 30, joggled edges of plates would give the most pleasing form in a small boat since all plating would be flush. There are features to lapped plating which might not appeal to the persons unaccustomed to seeing the beauty of fair strakes.

WELDING

Aluminum is often considered a difficult material to weld. It is, however, one of the most readily weldable of all materials.

Because the temperatures used in welding aluminum alloys are not within the visible light range, it is difficult to determine when the melting temperature is approached. This is not the case with other metals, welders knowing by color when the material has reached a stage of weldability. When aluminum is overheated, the alloys show a tendency to collapse and heat applied by welding is rapidly spread through the adjacent metal due to high thermal conductivity.

Gas welding normally is by the oxyhydrogen or by the oxyacetylene process. Although these methods are suitable for small work, production methods require the use of arc welding. The two above-mentioned methods are to be preferred to the oxybutane, oxypropane, or the oxynatural gas conditions since they are faster in their welding speeds. Five per cent silicon rod is best for marine use for strength and corrosion resistance. The welding flame should be a neutral flame preheated from 300° to 500° F. Gas welds should be made in one pass. Gas welding can be successfully worked on plates as small as 1/32" to unlimited thicknesses. Suitable edge preparation and preheating are determined by the material used. The weld surface should be free from oil, grease and dirt.

The method most suitable for marine work, because of its less cumbersome equipment, is the arc welding method. There are basically four processes of arc welding. The three general types are metal arc, carbon arc, and atomic hydrogen. The fourth process, the inert gas shielded arc, was developed primarily for the welding of magnesium and is and has been applied successfully to aluminum.

Arc welding has its limitations as well as its advantages. It is very difficult to weld material less than ⅛" in thickness in production. For fillet welds, the minimum electrode size is ⅛", and for gas-tight and vapor-tight welds, 3/16" to ¼" seems to be the recommended minimum thickness of plate. Its advantage, or course, lies in the fact that very little edge preparation is necessary. The American Bureau of Shipping recommendations in welding of steel are equally applicable to the welding of aluminum. In ¼" steel plate, a V-butt welded both sides will have 100 per cent joint efficiency under ABS; an identical weld in aluminum will result in only 80-90 per cent joint efficiency, being 10 to 20 per cent less than the developed strength of the parent metal.

A good welder will do well to average an 85 per cent efficient joint in the welding of aluminum alloys. Under laboratory conditions, an additional five per cent can be expected. In similar thicknesses of steel and aluminum, it is equally necessary to V or double-V plates. In aluminum, backing strips are always necessary when complete penetration is required. This backing strip may be of copper, asbestos, or steel, with a groove at the butt so that there will be space for flux. Preheating is necessary on thick plates in order to maintain the weld puddle, and also aids in reducing porosity, rapid cooling, and distortion. Jigging is about the same as for steel, although heat loss should be minimized.

In the metal arc method, heavily coated electrodes are used. The flux coating rapidly dissolves the outside film of the base metal to a slag of lower density than the molten weld metal, stabilizes the arc, and covers the weld, preventing excessive oxidation during cooling. The reverse polarity or positive electrodes method is usually used. The electrode should have approximately the same compositions as the base metal; however, five per cent silicon is better for corrosion resistance. The metal arc method of welding aluminum is approximately three times faster than the same process in steel. There is no necessity for weaving the electrodes in butt welding. The arc is struck in the same manner as a match is struck; if struck by touching the metal as in steel, the electrode will stick. Short arcs from ⅛″ to 3/16″ are preferable because of their stability. A long arc apparently has a tendency to become wild and splatter.

In starting a new electrode, it is best to start about ½″ back of the crater in order to avoid burning the plate. Electrodes should be held nearly vertical; however, some forward slant is not objectionable. Excessive slant causes porosity and splatter. In beveled plates, a back and forth movement is to be preferred to a weaving one, although weaving is permissible in fillet welds. It is always desirable to make single passes; however, when multiple passes are required, it is necessary to make sure that each pass is clean before a succeeding pass is made.

Manual carbon arc is usually limited to plates of less than ⅜″ in thickness. It is essentially the same as that used for steel. In carbon arc welding the carbon electrode is normally the negative pole, the filler metal being forward to the arc frame in the same manner as gas welding. The lighter the coating, on the electrode, the faster the welding speed. Automatic carbon-arc welding can be used to great advantages on decks and flats where long continuous welds are desirable. In all carbon arc welding, a backing strip should be used. After the weld is completed, slag and flux must be removed.

Atomic hydrogen welding of aluminum alloys results in a satisfactory quality of weld. Unlike the other methods of arc welding, the arc does not supply the heat. Instead, the heat generated in the arc is transferred by hydrogen to the work. The molecules of hydrogen separate into their component parts, atoms, as gas passes through the arc from jets around tungsten electrodes. The gas in the atomic state is displaced with molecular hydrogen under pressure and is edged out of the arc. When heat of the arc passes, the hydrogen atoms recombine into the normal molecules giving up their heat of disassociation. It is this heat that produces the resulting welding temperature. The weld is affected in an atmosphere of hydrogen and oxidation of molten metal cannot occur.

The primary advantage of atomic hydrogen is that welding speeds are fast. Fuller metal is usually required in heavy plates, and is always required in fillet welds to avoid undercutting. Because of the speed of this method, distortion is kept at a minimum. The electric current values used with this method of welding are much lower in comparison with the other arc methods.

Inert gas shielded welding is very similar to the atomic hydrogen process in that it employs a tungsten electrode and a gas that shields the welded metal from the atmosphere. Instead of hydrogen, helium or argon is used as they are inert gases. These gases do not disassociate like hydrogen. The filler metal and weld puddle are shielded in the inert gas envelope so successfully that flux is not necessary when proper equipment and techniques are used. Slag entrapment is minimized and, when no flux is used, flux entrapment is entirely eliminated. Stabilized alternating current is used when flux is not used. Where argon is used with AC welding, it must be of a very high purity—about 99.8 per cent argon to nitrogen or better.

Helium, until recently, had not been as successful as argon due to low grade of tungsten electrodes; however, using helium and DC current, the weld is accomplished in much shorter time. This is due to a more concentrated and hotter arc. There is greater control over fillet welds by this method than when argon is used. Helium must be of a high purity—99.99 per cent—which is available commercially. Cleanliness of the portion to be welded is very important and should be achieved by a manual or power abrasive which removes dirt effectively without scratching the surface as a wire brush will.

Of primary importance to the designer of small craft, of course, is the satisfactory welding of joints which he has designed. This can be accomplished only by qualified welding operators. The U.S. Navy and the American Bureau of Shipping have welder qualification tests in steel; the Navy has one in aluminum. These tests or similar tests should be given to all welders working on any vessel. The qualifications usually specify whether the welder is competent in vertical, flat and overhead positions, and a test plate is made up and cut, testing the weld by guide bends, free bends, tensile break tests, etc. These methods will establish the ductility, soundness and strength of the weld.

Since all welding cannot be so examined, radiography or X-ray tests should be used on all important seams and especially on joints of the main structure. The fluorescent method of inspection can also be used, but is not as satisfactory as the radiography test.

It is well to remember that most aluminum alloys can be brazed. Some are more adaptable than others; however, their use on small craft or large is not to be recommended in preference to welding or riveting. With regard to significant non-structural parts that are customarily brazed in other materials, the author can see no objection to brazing similar parts when made of aluminum.

Fabrications, Sub-Assembly and Erection

Because of the lightness of aluminum, larger sub-assemblies may be fabricated and erected by the small boatyard which will reduce labor cost in that assembly can be to the convenience of the worker. Also, special jigging can be simplified which is not always the case when the boat is erected in a similar manner to wooden boats.

In the combining of the various sub-assemblies, methods of joining are usually by temporarily bolting two assemblies together. Usually in rivet construction, the use of erection bolts merely employs the same holes as a finished rivet will use. The possibilities of sub-assembly should always be investigated by architects who are connected with a building yard.

Mold Loft Considerations

In metal design, since all dimensions are molded dimensions, mold loft work is considerably reduced in the laying down and taking off of frames and plates, the methods applicable to steel being equally applicable to aluminum. Because of aluminum's light weight, it is often desirable to use the actual sheet metal rather than to make a wooden template. It would be possible in small fabricating yards to use a bending machine located in the mold loft, so frames could be bent and checked without having to make wooden templates since heat is not always necessary in the bending of shapes. Aluminum should be marked with a pencil rather than scribed with an awl which will permanently mar the surface.

Storage of Aluminum

As with any other material, aluminum should be kept under cover. Water-marking, which is a staining of the metal, is caused by water dripping or standing for periods of time on unprotected aluminum. There is no harmful effect other than surface stain caused by this water-marking; and, when as in most marine instances, the finish is to be painted, the extra precautions against water-marking need not be taken.

All aluminum alloys possess a natural coating of aluminum oxide which, according to alloy, varies in thickness and color. Usually it is very thin—almost transparent—and colorless, and is useful in that it provides protection to the aluminum surface. This oxide is such that it is a natural resistor to corrosion and chemical attack since it is inert. The oxide caused by aluminum and its alloying elements is in the form of gray and white crystals and is always a mixture of various sulphates and carbonates and causes no effects to the mechanical properties of the material. The alloy, 52-8, which is one of the most suitable for marine use, because of its resistance to corrosion, has great amounts of these crystals due to magnesium salt formations.

When a yard receives a shipment of aluminum, it should promptly give each temper an identifying mark since they all look alike.

FINISHING AND PAINTING OF ALUMINUM

In the painting of aluminum, paints with a lead pigment base should be avoided. Zinc chromate is best for its corrosion inhibitive properties. The thickness of the primer coat should be measured in mills by a General Electric film thickness gauge or magnetic type gauge which has been calibrated against the G.E. gauge over metal of the same thickness if possible. The interior, when used with zinc chromate, should equal 4.5 mills; decks and superstructure, 7 mills; bottom, 7 mills, topsides, 6 mills; wet voids, ballast, tanks, etc. should be coated with bituplastic. Brushed on coats are to be preferred to spray coats.

Practically all marine paints may then be applied over the primer coat. It is possible to employ many standard finishes on aluminum—artificial wood, leather, hammered, grained, etc. are standard finishes for interior paneling.

There are two types of aluminum pigments—the leafing and non-leafing. They have very limited use in marine work, the heat-resistant aluminum pigments being widely used on steam piping, boiler fronts, engines, motors, etc.

REPAIR

The repair of aluminum is very similar in all instances to steel. There are, at present, very few places along the coast that will do aluminum welding repairs, usually because they lack the electrodes necessary to do the job. However, it may be well for those who contemplate owning aluminum vessels or plan to design them, to reserve a small portion of the stowage space for a repair kit which would enable any yard equipped to work in metal to repair the aluminum hull.

Unlike steel, corrosion is not a repair factor; therefore, replacement of large plates due to corrosion will never occur. Punctures and denting, however, can readily be repaired by anyone familiar with metal working. Care should be exercised in obtaining identical compositions in the replacement or matching of aluminum. The repaired portion should be well painted.

COST AND VALUE ANALYSIS

The design of special parts should be sufficiently fluid to enable the substitution of similar but equal quality parts that may be furnished by a sub-contractor or vendor working in conjunction with the building yard. The designer must always analyze, regardless of the medium with which he is working, the strongest and most suitable shape which will, in most instances, be the most economical.

The value of structural analysis is a never-ending task for designers. A full knowledge of all accessories and finishes is necessary in the advent of a new product on the market that it be evaluated for present or future uses and, on the basis of this evaluation, it be accepted or rejected. The ability of a designer to save money at the expense of beauty, structural soundness, etc., would not be consistent with the over-all function of any design. A thorough understanding of the materials with which the designer must work gained through experience in applying these materials will greatly aid in the creative imagination necessary to simplify the engineering phase of design. To eliminate and/or simplify is always the problem confronting the designer-engineer. Those who are truly dedicated to design and design engineering of small craft (and this may be considered true in almost any field) should be able to recognize, consciously and subconsciously, the hidden, as well as the evident, values of all materials, regardless how insignificant. It is not an 8-hour-a-day vocation, but a 24-hour-a-day avocation.

FABRICATION, SUB-ASSEMBLY, AND ERECTION

I have included several structural notes which are preferably prepared as a drawing and attached with each design.

1. Structural material is to be aluminum alloy unless otherwise noted.

2. All aluminum shall be cleaned except material furnaced during the progress of the work and shall be painted with zinc chromate. Where possible, when steel is used in connection with aluminum, it shall be galvanized and separated from the aluminum with a layer of permagum.

3. Calking edges of plates and shapes are to be planed

or sawn. Minimum amount necessary for calking is to be removed from shapes that are not cut down for weight saving. Care is to be taken to maintain proper edge distance from centers of rivets.

4. Where plates of different thicknesses are butt welded and thickness differences exceeds ⅛″, the thicker plate is to be beveled 30° unless otherwise indicated.

5. Frames are to be spaced apart.

6. Frame line is on the midship side of the floor or bulkhead unless otherwise noted.

7. Dimensions are given from the frame line unless otherwise noted.

8. Dimensions locating longitudinal flat bar, T-bar, angle bar, and I-beam sections are to the edge of the web nearest the centerline of the vessel unless otherwise noted.

9. Dimensions locating transverse flat bar, T-bar, angle bar and I-beam sections are to the edge of the web nearest midship unless otherwise noted.

10. Molded line frames, deck longitudinals are to the inboard side of the sheer and underside of the decks.

11. Members to be connected by T-joints are to be neatly fitted and those members to be connected by fillet welds shall have a clearance not to exceed 3/32″ for straight surfaces and 5/32″ for curved surfaces.

12. Where clearance between two members to be connected by fillet welds is greater than 1/16″, the size of the weld shall be the indicated size plus clearance.

13. Where single and double groove welds are not backed up by a strap, the root of the weld shall be chipped out to sound continuous metal after sufficient weld metal has been deposited on one side and before any welding on the opposite side has been undertaken.

14. Butt welds shall, in general, be made before both members of the joint are riveted or permanently welded in place. In special cases approved by the designer and/or the American Bureau of Shipping, where circumstances make it impracticable to comply with the above requirement, an unstrapped butt, which is not free to move, may be welded provided its members are unsecured on either side of the joint for a distance of not less than 18″.

15. On joints involving welds affecting the tightness of gas and fuel oil tanks are to be multiple pass or grooved welds depending on thickness of material.

16. All welded butts in rolled sections are to have a single V welded both sides in both flange and web regardless of thickness of material.

17. Where single V joints welded both sides in plates are indicated on plans, double V joints may be substituted and vice versa to suit working conditions when material is not over 1″ thick.

18. Where single V welded both sides are indicated on the plans, then bevels can be on either the near or far side, whichever is more suitable for the building yard.

19. Fillet welds shall be extended around the ends of the member to form a U whenever possible.

20. Riveting occurring near welding shall be done after all welding in that vicinity has been completed except that structure may be welded to butt and seam straps and to riveting straps after rivets have been driven and where otherwise specifically approved by the designer.

21. Clearance between the nominal diameter of the rivet and the rivet hole shall not exceed 1/32″.

22. All rivet holes are to be punched or drilled ⅛″ small

and reamed to size after work has been fitted to place on the vessel unless otherwise noted on the plan.

23. Butt and edges of plates and butts of angles and strap joints shall fit closely together after being riveted. Calking pieces shall not be fitted in any such joints in water-tight or oil-tight work.

24. At intersections of intercostal shapes (web, etc.) with structural members, a snipe of minimum practical size shall be provided in the web of the intercostal members where required to clear completed welds at fillet and bosom of structural shapes, at projecting stem or T-bars cut from I-beams, etc. For snipes in way of water-tight work, see note under No. 26.

25. Where beam and stiffener brackets are built up of T-sections, fillet plates are to be fitted in the throat of same only where the opening exceeds 1½″.

26. All non-tight structure including deck beams and stiffeners in way of juncture of tight bulkheads and decks shall be sniped to permit continuous weld of bulkheads to deck unless specifically shown or noted otherwise on structural drawings.

27. All vessels built, under the rules of the American Bureau of Shipping are subject to radiographic inspection of welds.

The author wishes to express his appreciation to the Reynolds Metals Company, the Aluminum Company of America, and to Mr. David MacIntyre, N.A., in charge of the Marine Sales Division, ALCOA for their valued assistance.

Chapter Seventeen

SOME STUDIES
OF VIBRATION PROBLEMS

By GERALD T. WHITE

ONE of the sad commentaries of boating is that few owners take any pride in the amazing mechanism that propels their boat. That is, when this mechanism happens to be an engine.

The sail boat enthusiast boasts of his rig and pridefully exhibits any little gadget he has devised to make the running rigging run or the standing rigging stand. If he can raise a diaper-sized bit of fabric to the breeze he does so and calls the result a spanker spoofsail. He ends up writing an article for the boating magazines all about his invention. But, for some reason, he is bitterly ashamed of the fact that, soaking somewhere down in the cellar of the boat there dwells an engine that is considered the black sheep of her owner's boating family.

The one man in a million who takes pride in the marvel that lives in the bilge is scornfully called a "grease ball" or a "stinkboater" by those who follow the iron men and wooden ship tradition. Is it any wonder that most designers stick the poor engine out of sight when the boatbuilder's sales department explains that an engine is something horrible that should be hidden like the fact that your grandmother was addicted to straight corn likker washed down with a snake venom chaser.

If the foregoing is true we find that machinery should be neither seen, heard nor felt. A marine engine is the leprous mechanism that should be equipped with a sign warning, "Unclean! Unclean!" Just as long as we are faced with sales managers and with owners who think of boating only in the terms of sunlight glinting the summer seas we must make every effort to make the engine as unobtrusive as possible. For the benefit of the eyes we hide the machine down-cellar beneath air tight hatches. We muffle its exhaust and sound insulate its already cramped quarters so that the dainty ears of the owner and his guests will always hear the call for cocktails but never the groans of protest from the machinery.

Thus we have done a pretty good job of everything but the feeling of shimmy that is found obnoxious by many owners. The machine can no longer be seen nor heard— as an aside I would like to add that it can no longer be reached for servicing either—but its wiggles can still be felt by the softies on deck who complain bitterly. It seems that we must take the shakes out of the job, completely emasculating it of every action aside from the important point that it is the one thing that gets the boat from here to there and back again.

The modern marine engine has been well balanced at the factory. At least we see pictures of white-coated engineers balancing each piston, rod and cotter pin on a precision scale. One has to be a confirmed cynic to doubt that every moving part is not so carefully checked and double checked. But if we are naive and believe that every moving part received this loving care we are still faced with the fact that the machine is put into a boat on engine beds that have been shortened and cut away to the limit lest they interfere with something the sales department wants to put over.

An example of this may be of some interest. Not long ago I was called to inspect a boat that had just been rebuilt. She had a pair of six-cylinder engines jammed into a space that had formerly been crowded with a single screw machine. With the aid of the trouble light I found a place where it was possible to glimpse an engine bed. There appeared the head of a large nail where a through bolt should have been. The first thought was that the bed had been temporarily nailed into position while the bolt holes were being bored. Being of a suspicious nature, I asked about the nail and found that the new beds had, literally, been nailed down on the top of the bed; the inboard beds of the twin engines being nailed to the former single screw bed. My suggestion that the two engines be taken out and through bolts put in was met with considerable ire on the part of the boatbuilder. He argued that the 650-pound engines could be placed on a couple of soap boxes and run. In fact he offered to do exactly that if we would come up into his shop.

His argument almost convinced the owner until I pointed out that both engines would be of no possible use unless they had thrust enough to push the boat and that neither would be on soap boxes on the shop floor. At sea, the machines would be trying to push themselves forward off the beds while, at the same time, they would be swaying from side to side as the boat rolled. It was not until we had actually gone to sea in the boat that the builder and the owner were convinced. Those beds wobbled around so that one engine cracked its fuel pipe and we had to come home on its jitterbugging brother.

Many attempts have been made to overcome engine vibration. It is not part of our professional work to go into the balancing of the moving parts. They must be left for the factory. Possibly with an idea that they were helping us to design less jittery boats, many marine motor firms installed rubber mountings on the engine supporting arms. If anything worse has ever been offered to the marine purchaser, I fail to find it recorded. The argument is that the rubber mountings allow the engine to wiggle but the jitters will not be communicated to the hull. The machine is supposed to sit down in the dark and damp and shimmy away without our beloved clients being aware of it. All of which is complete nonsense. To insulate the shimmies from the rest of the boat would require flexible water inlet pipes, flexible fuel lines, flexible exhaust pipes, flexible reverse controls, flexible throttle gimmicks and a flexible connection between engine and propeller shaft.

All that would be mighty, mighty difficult to obtain. At best the control linkage would wiggle at one end and be quiet at the other. In-between the two extremes we would have noise at every joint. My personal experience has been that rubber mountings have one good purpose. After removal some of them can be reshaped and shoved under the shop door to keep it from swinging in the wind. They also are fairly efficient as paper weights.

Mention of such mountings brings to mind that the modern marine engine is usually supported on four legs. Many such machines have provisions for only one lag bolt per leg. Some have two holes. Yet you wonder why they shimmy. Compare these machines with the traditional marine engine. Such machines had a steel bed plate that extended from the after edge of the flywheel to the coupling and supported the engine and reverse gear in proper manner. These engines actually reinforced the bed logs. One would never think of turning out a job with a multi-cylinder engine without putting at least six lags or hanger bolts on each side. If you want to see the difference, take an old soap box and knock the bottom out. Now nail the bottom back again with one nail in each corner of the bottom and start kicking that box around. It will take but little punishment before it cries "Uncle." But if you nail the bottom down along the sides with a fastening every few inches you have something that will take a beating.

When the four-legged engines first came out, their legs were of the same length and installers who knew their stuff used to bolt an angle iron to the legs and then set the angle on top of the bed logs and bolt it down. The result was pretty good. But then they found that long legs in front and short legs behind saved a couple of cents in making proper engine beds so it was no longer possible to use the angle iron stunt. This is where we are today with the majority of our engines.

The old story is that the engine girders should be extended as far forward and aft as possible. It is still a good idea, for it adds longitudinal stiffness to our hulls. A girder is a plank on edge and unless the pair of planks on edge are braced laterally they are going to wobble from side to side no matter whether they are six feet long or three times that. Getting in the lateral bracing is a thankless job. Floor lines have been dropped into close association with the keel. The idea of a nice oaken brace showing above the cabin floor has been known to drive a sales manager into cutting out paper dolls. We try to tie the beds to bulkheads—and then cut the bulkhead in half for a doorway. Try to run braces to a bilge stringer and you find a tank is in the way. Try to reduce the side wiggle by using 4 inch material for the beds and the production department will sadly point out that such a bed would add $7.36 to the cost of the $12,000 boat, obviously limiting free enterprise and also limiting your take home pay to zero unless you get such crackpot ideas out of your bonnet.

If you remember back to the one-lung engine days you will recall the beds that ran athwartships. They were set apart only the length of the engine and were shaped on the bottom to the inside contour of the hull. They were not too hot as thrust absorbers but those little engines didn't have enough thrust to matter. In spite of their single cylinder and a complete lack of precision balancing at the factory there was a minimum of vibration throughout the hull for the simple reason that the engines were firmly bolted to the beds and the beds, in turn, were as much a part of the basic hull structure as the planking itself. The vibration of the engine was so thoroughly distributed that no unpleasant shimmy was found anywhere from the bow to the stern.

The same idea can still be carried on with the modern engines and hulls provided we consider that the engine foundation must be an integral part of the hull framing;

construction that must be fitted and fastened just as thoroughly as we now attach a stem knee to the keel. One way to accomplish that would be with the use of oversized floor timbers spaced no more than 12 inches apart for a distance equal to approximately one-third the length of the boat. There is nothing new in this idea of carrying engine beds on heavy floor timbers but our floor timbers have seldom had sufficient lateral spread. Unless the boats were very broad and lacking in deadrise, the floor timber having a straight top did not extend far enough on each side of the centerline to properly distribute lateral shimmy.

However, the objective is not difficult to find providing we are willing to spend a few dollars more per boat. Instead of cutting the upper edge of the floor timber parallel with the lateral waterline we can, by using wider material, curve the upper edge so that the arms reach out for several feet on each side of the centerline. On a bent-frame boat one excellent way of accomplishing this would be to set the floor timber on top of the frame and then steam bend another frame on top of the floor timber and extending up the original frame to the sheer line.

On V-bottom boats the same general idea could be carried out by using a thicker siding for the bottom frames in the way of the engine bed, having the floor timbers the same sided dimension and then using marine plywood gussets to extend the construction well up the side of the boat. In either case, precision workmanship is an absolute necessity. Sloppy joints destroy every advantage of such construction. Just as a chain is only as strong as its weakest link, a structure designed to absorb shimmy is only as efficient as its loosest joint.

Of course any such bed design must have some longitudinal members to actually carry the engine hold-down bolts and to obviate the tilting effect of both ahead and astern thrust. We use such longitudinals in our regulation beds but, in most boats with rising buttocks aft, we find that the girder cannot be extended far abaft the engine lest it run out into a featheredge. In fact the depth of floor timbers aft become so small that the entire idea falls flat on its face. This would not be true if we used a girder steam bent, or sawn, to the approximate contour of the buttock lines. Such a girder, halved into the suggested floor timbers, would form a non-vibrating structure that could be truly said to cradle the engine.

In the way of the engine the floor timbers would have to be cut away to allow room for the oil pan and lower base. Therein lies the basic weakness in the idea but there is no reason to believe that the cut-outs would be any more extensive than they are now. Here we could turn to steel plates or plywood for gussets to brace the cut away portions of the floor timbers. The minimum amount of cut-out could be obtained by careful designing-in the location of the engine so that the deepest portion of the oil pans clears the floor timbers as little as possible.

There is no question but what such construction would be more costly nor that it would take up more bilge room. On the other hand it has some advantages. Wing tanks, for example, could be supported from the cradle instead of hung from deckbeams or nestled into scrap lumber cleats attached to frames. The same thing applies to the storage batteries and perhaps to the auxiliary generator, oil tanks and tool racks. The more weight that could be carried by the cradle the more free it would be of vibration. It would form the base for the various engine controls which often span the distance from engine to bulkhead without any form of steadying bearing. If the controls were led downward to the cradle top and along that top to the control position we would obviate much noise as well as obtain a steadier running engine.

One of the sources of noise is the linkage of a reverse gear. Many boats are so arranged that the reverse control could be nothing more than the simple lever extending through a slot in the bridge deck. No rattle, no lost motion, no problem at all except that the control station will look like that of a boat and not be similar to a pipe organ. Rather than the simple lever we too often find multiple links and arms eventually leading to the side of the binnacle box where a beautiful little onyx knob is placed. It looks very neat but suffers from severe shakes plus calling for lubrication which it probably will not get. For throttle, choke and spark controls the push-pull Bowden wire cannot be excelled providing both wire and tube are of bronze or stainless steel. Ordinary steel wire run through an electroplated flexible tube is bound to cause trouble. But even with the best Bowden wire it is necessary to clip the tubing at frequent intervals, especially where it is bent. In theory there is no lost motion in a push-pull control but there is plenty of it if the tube is allowed to hang in a loop.

We hear much about hydraulic controls. Basically they are nothing but lengths of tubing bent as required and having a piston at each end. The line is filled with glycerine or similar non-freezing and relatively thick liquid. Moving the piston at one end results in a corresponding movement of the piston at the opposite end. All such rigs carry liquid under pressure and require stuffing boxes and tight fitting moving parts. Whether these disadvantages outweigh the simplicity of installation and non-rattling virtues is an open question. What we cannot deny is that all such rigs are expensive although any clever handyman can use hydraulic motor car brake fittings which are obtainable at a fraction of the cost of the marine gimmicks.

As a rule, the engine is blamed for all the noise aboard a boat, noises which often may be traced to the galley, toolbox, steering gear or even to lockers where general duffel has been dumped in a helter-skelter fashion. A story in this relation may be appropriate. One of the crack ocean liners had a noise problem that drove her officers and her designers almost frantic. Strangely enough the noise and actual shakes came only during the night. Certain engine room pumps were run during those hours and the blame was placed on them. They were remounted but the trouble persisted.

After months of search the answer was found. The ship was large enough to have a passenger elevator. During the day and evening the elevator was in almost constant use, but after midnight there was little business on this vertical railway. The night operator found that the car had a tendency to settle slightly below deck level. When there were passengers constantly entering or leaving the car he monkeyed with the controls to maintain the proper level. But during the hours when the trips were few and far between he allowed the car to settle a few inches onto supports at the bottom of the shaft. This allowed the supporting cables to loosen just enough so that, as the ship rolled, they swung gently and set up vibration that was passed along to the staterooms on the upper decks. The solution came when the operator was ordered to keep the car supported by its cables rather than by the bumpers at the shaft bottom.

Some cases of this kind have no solution. The famous Hudson River steamboat *Mary Powell* had a shimmy and rattle in the vicinity of what we politely call the ladies' retiring room. The owners tore out and replaced bulkheads and put supporting straps around various pipes and fittings to no avail. The old girl simply refused to allow her female passengers to perform certain necessary tasks in comfort. It had one good feature; no one remained in there longer than necessary. One could get a bit ribald about the case but we will try to keep this discussion on a higher plane.

In another case, a large and luxury-type cruising yacht suffered from a banging noise particularly in head seas. Prolonged search finally placed the blame on a fresh water tank but the cause was not found until the tank was removed and torn apart. One of the swash plates had been improperly installed, the rivet holes in the plate flange having been bored well over size. As the water sloshed fore and aft the plate slammed back and forth and the noise transmitted throughout the entire plumbing system, seeming to be greater at some of the lavatory faucets than at the tank itself.

Nowadays we hear a great deal about sound insulation. Various types of low-priced wall board are tacked around engine compartments. Such noise traps can be efficient, but unfortunately, they can also be used to cover shoddy workmanship and to form unventilated pockets ideal for the development of rot. One builder was quite frank about the use of perforated anti-noise board on the under-

side of his deckhouse roof. Questioned about the amount
of noise that would be reflected from the underside of the
roof he agreed that the covering had but two good points:
(A) it formed a sales argument and, (B) his deck beams
were left unfinished and unpainted. Instead of having to
paint the underside of the roof and the sides and bottoms
of the beams he tacked up the wall board with some battens over the seams, the whole business having been pre-
painted and varnished on the bench.

One cannot consider the vibration problems without
realizing that the number and quality of the fastenings is
of vital importance. Back in the days when the journey-
man boatbuilder was a real artisan we had boats with
riveted fastenings not only in the keel and frame but also
copper rivets holding planking to the frame. Copper or
galvanized rod was furnished in long lengths and cut off
and headed up by the builder as required. Even galvanized iron rod, if touched up with red lead and then wood
plugged, provided a fastening that lasted for half a century.

Today, the boat shop labor is of a quality that prohibits
the use of rivets. The men who know of boatbuilding as
a life work are engaged as foremen over a crew of wood
butchers that cannot be trusted to draw up a rivet to the
proper tension.

So we turn to screws, an excellent fastening medium
but one that requires considerable skill to do properly.
To save precious man hours, we use electric screw drivers
which cannot compensate for the varying softness of
woods. Before the mechanical driver will let go it may
drive the screw head almost through soft cedar. The old-
timer could tell when a screw was properly home by the

torsion on his screw driver plus a "feeling" that cannot be defined nor taught except through experience.

I recall the days at the old Seabury plant when the men took pride in their work. A screw that had gone in too far created an immediate sensation. It was quickly removed, a tapered spile driven in, the countersink plugged and another fastening bored alongside. Can we believe that the same sort of care goes into the construction of all of our boats today?

A poor fastening will allow vibration which, like a cancerous growth, spreads to all nearby areas. When screws are used it is not sufficient to tighten the screw. A wood screw does nothing more than tap a hole in the wood and follow those threads. Once it is tightened beyond a certain point, or removed and replaced, the threads are totally or partially destroyed. Vibration then is given an opportunity to increase the size of all surrounding holes and loosen the fastenings.

It is the writer's belief that the use of throughbolts with lock washers and nuts could become universal. One may criticize the expense of using bolts for plank fastenings but there might be some savings to counteract. For one thing the hole through both plank and frame would be of the same size. Nuts could be put on with speed wrenches. There would be no loss from splitting of either plank or frame, a common complaint when a tapered screw is used. It may be a minor matter but it occurs that, in quantity production, certain interior work such as ceiling, shelves, etc. could be more easily fastened by having the planking bolts long enough at the specific locations, so that the joiner work could be slipped over the excess length of bolt and another nut run on.

One thing seems certain, a loose fastening could be easily tightened by anyone able to hold a wrench. There would be no threads in the wood to be destroyed and no splits along the line of fastenings. If you have ever removed the planking of a screw-fastened boat the chances are that you have noted that the row of fastenings has started a split along a large number of frames. Putting in a new screw will never solve such a problem. In fact, it may make it worse and thereby increase the vibration between parts to eventually cause enough damage to entail major repairs.

There would be universal agreement were we to say that good construction—say bronze fastenings instead of black iron fastenings—cost money. Yet how many builders worthy of mention will use black iron bolts? They increase the cost of their boats in a sincere effort to provide a measure of quality, but in many cases, they stop at a point where the better construction links in with the sales department's talk.

The novice purchaser is apt to ask for non-ferrous fastenings and he may call the police if he finds he did not get them in his boat. On the other hand such things as vibration cannot be reduced to an ordinary sales pitch. Ask the salesman if the boat has an oak keel and you give him something he can get his teeth into. He must reply either "yes" or "no." Ask him if the boat vibrates and you know right away that he will give a negative reply. What you call an unpleasant shimmy he will laughingly call the "trembling of the boat to be off." An engineer can measure and chart vibration; others can only state as a personal opinion whether it is unpleasant or even disastrous. Yet the fact remains that all vibration must be unpleasant and all of it must place shearing and tensile stresses on every item in the construction.

It is the hope of the writer that this paper may stimulate our readers into a more thorough study of the subject matter.

Chapter Eighteen

NOISE AND VIBRATION: ITS PREVENTION AND CURE

By RAYMOND T. SOREL

I WOULD LIKE to define what I mean by noise and vibration so that we'll all be thinking of the same thing
while we are talking about it. Noise is any unwanted
sound; vibration is the movement of a structure so low in
frequency that we can't hear it. If you think about it for
a minute, you'll see that vibration is noise but so low in
frequency that it doesn't usually bother us. It is important
to us, though, because it can cause damage.

Noise is the crazy, mixed-up child of the science of
acoustics. It's very difficult to make predictions about it.
It appears in strange places and does unexpected things.
It sometimes defies analysis. All we have learned about it
is some of the conditions where it appears, and a few
situations where we can make it go away—or at least be

a little less troublesome. There is no neat formula that you can plug numbers into and grind out an answer. What I intend to do is describe some of the ways noise is produced and some of the ways it is reduced. I hope you will get an idea of the general principles of reducing noise and vibration so that you can apply these principles in your design work. You will see that it takes a bit of imagination to do this but most small craft designers seem to be blessed with plenty of imagination.

A Boat Hull as a Musical Instrument

Think of a boat as a musical instrument; a violin, for example. If you bow or pluck the strings of the violin you get a sound out of it. Does the sound come from the string? No, it comes from the box that the strings are mounted on. We know you wouldn't get much sound from a string stretched between two nails driven into a log. Much of the noise that exists in a boat is excited by the engine. This is the thing we must remember—the engine excites the hull of the boat and the hull produces the noise. Even the noise you get from the exhaust and intake are often associated with parts of the engine or even cavities in the engine that are excited by the flow of gases.

Why does a metal hull sound noisier than a wooden hull? The reason is that the wood soaks up the noise faster than metal, especially the higher frequencies. In the immediate neighborhood of a running engine, a wood hull may be vibrating just as much or more than a similar hull made of metal. This gives us a clue to one method of reducing noise.

THREE BASIC METHODS OF REDUCING NOISE

There are actually three methods of cutting down on noise. We can get the manufacturer to make his engines so perfectly fitted and so well balanced that the engine doesn't do any exciting to speak of.

Or, we could cushion the engine so well that no matter how much it wants to shake and vibrate, the motion cannot get to the hull. This is the method some outboard motor manufacturers have used recently with considerable success.

The last method is to let the engine vibrate all it wants to, but convert the vibration energy into some other form of energy, such as heat, so that it is no longer available to produce noise.

It is too much to expect of engine manufacturers that they will make engines so perfect that they are not noisy —even if anybody could afford them. The business of shock mounting or isolating the engine introduces alignment problems, among other things. Still, this is a method to keep in mind when installing auxiliary machinery such as generators and pumps. The last method, changing the vibrational energy into heat, is economical and practical.

THE ENGINE AS AN EXCITING FORCE

Since the engine or engines propelling the boat seems to be the principle exciting source of noise, this seems to be a logical place to start in reducing the noise. The manufacturer in choosing a place to put the mountings for fastening the engine to the boat at first chose those the easiest to manufacture. In many cases, this was an extension of the block where the top of the crankcase bisects the main bearings of the crankshaft. At first glance, this seems to be a reasonable enough place. The torsional vibrations certainly tend to rotate the engine around the crankshaft. But if we could toss the engine into the air like we would flip a coin, we find the engine tends to revolve around its center of gravity. In most engines the center of gravity is several inches above the crankshaft. The first thing to do in mounting an engine to reduce vibration is to mount the engine in such a way that a plane connecting the mounts passes through the center of gravity of the engine. This is so important that it is worth repeating: "The engine should be mounted in such a way that a plane connecting the mounts passes through its center of gravity."

ENGINE MOUNTS IN SHEAR

The engine mounts should be placed so that the stress in the mounting bolts are in shear. Flexible mounts of any kind are more effective in soaking up vibrational energy in this direction than in compression. However, in talking about engine mounts we are not necessarily restricted to talking about rubber mountings. It is obvious from these recommendations that "auxiliary" mounts will need to be built if we expect to reduce noise and vibration. That is, we will have to make a sort of frame in which to mount the engine which will have itself mounting structures that will pass through the engine's center of gravity. Do not weld this frame together! It should be bolted and each piece of the framework separated by a gasket material such as reinforced asbestos, perhaps 1/32 inch thick. While the vibrations that take place in structural materials are very small compared to the amplitudes of the same energy in air, these vibrations take place with an almost irresistible force. The force is great enough to compress steel. Therefore, we must change this powerful force, that moves so slightly, into heat. The bolt in the joints of any structure cannot be made tight enough to make the structure vibrate as a single unit. The asbestos gasket then creates the friction necessary to convert these movements into heat. This is the key to the secret of quieting hulls. It explains why riveted steel hulls are invariably quieter than welded hulls. Even rivets driven hot cannot force a hull to vibrate as a single unit. There is still movement in between the riveted joints.

BOLTED MEMBERS IN WELDED HULLS

When you build a metal hull, then, build into it as many structures as possible that are bolted together— and separate them with some sort of gasket material. As a suggestion you might try bolting gussets in place; if you have a steel bulkhead welded to the hull, cut out of it the biggest sheet you can and bolt it back in place with a backing strip separated by a gasket; bolt the deck house (if any) to a flange welded to the deck also separated by a waterproof gasket. You can think of many other ways to reduce noise this way. The more gasketed joints between the engine and the living spaces, the quieter the boat will be.

BALLAST AS QUIETING MATERIAL

In sailing boats it is often necessary to have some inside ballast. This ballast can be effectively used for reducing noise in metal boats. An engine mounted on a massive concrete bed is relatively quiet—at least it sounds quiet. The reason is that the weight of the concrete lowers the resonant frequency of the engine bed so much that you can't hear it. In a steel boat, it might be possible to put some concrete in the bilges around the engine mounts. We hope that you have already made up a bolted, gasketed, auxiliary mount as we described before. If your sailing auxiliary is made of aluminum, you will not be able to use concrete in the bilges because the aluminum will corrode in contact with concrete. But there is another substitute for inside ballast that we don't hear much about these days—boiler punchings and pitch. This should be an especially effective material because the vibrating hull will tend to shake the pitch in contact with it. The inertia of the boiler punchings will tend to keep them still and so the pitch will be flexed to some extent and the vibrational energy will be changed to heat.

ACOUSTICAL TREATMENT IN LIVING SPACES

How can we cut down on the noise of wave slap against the hull and the airborne noises that come from engine exhaust, radio, and drinking guests?

We're all familiar with acoustical tile used in homes and many public places. Here the sound penetrates the surface of the material and simply gets lost. Such materials have some uses on boats, but their effectiveness can be increased many times by a simple modification. The usual acoustical tile isn't a good choice for a boat because it is an organic material that holds moisture and is subject to rot. Fiberglas batts or boards are similar in density and texture but, being inorganic, are much more desirable on a boat. If we covered the interior of a boat with this fiberglas we would undoubtedly get a noticeable reduction in noise.

However, if we fastened a thin sheet of perforated aluminum to the fiberglas in such a way that no part of the perforated aluminum touches any part of the hull, we would find the noise reduction improved many fold. There are two reasons for this; first, the perforations allow the sound to penetrate the surface and get lost in the fiberglas. However, we still have a vibrating hull to contend with. In this case the hull is free to vibrate but the inertia of the perforated aluminum sheet causes the fiberglas to flex with the hull vibrations. The flexing fiberglas converts the energy into heat and thus the sound is lost in heat.

You might substitute asbestos or masonite pegboard for the perforated aluminum with equal success. You could also probably substitute Homasote or some other wallboard for the Fiberglas equally well. Your biggest problem will be in fastening this perforated septum to the fiberglas or wallboard and keeping it isolated from the hull. You might try inserting rubber grommets used by radiomen for feeding wires through metal chassis to isolate the septum, or bolts driven into contact with the hull.

THE PROPELLER SHAFT VIBRATION PROBLEM

We have been discussing noise for some time and it is time to mention vibration. Vibration usually gets to be called noise when its frequency gets over 25 to 30 cycles per second. Notice that this corresponds to frequencies up to about 1,800 cycles per minute or well within the speed range of most engines with something out of balance. What I mean to say is that an engine running at

1,800 rpms with an out-of-balance crankshaft will produce vibrations of 30 cycles per second. If we have a gear reduction of three to one we may also get vibrations at 10 cycles per second. If we have a three bladed propeller we may get an effect very much as though we had a bent propeller when the trouble is actually in the engine. This is what I meant when I stated earlier that noise and vibration at times defies analysis.

One of the principal causes of vibration is that some part of the boat is excited to resonance, usually by the engine. A propeller shaft may be just the right weight and length to be in resonance at 1,800 rpm. In such a circumstance, a six cylinder engine in the example mentioned before (i.e. 3 to 1 reduction gear, three bladed prop, etc.) could certainly cause a failure in the shaft if kept running for any length of time. In a severe case, such as this one, you could probably effect a partial cure by replacing the solid shaft with a hollow one broken into two or more flanged pieces. If the hollow shaft was the same weight as the solid one, it would be stiffer and would have a higher resonant frequency for this reason alone. If broken into two or more flanged pieces (of unequal length, by the way) the pieces would have a still higher frequency because of their smaller size and weight. Since the shaft would be bolted together at the flanged joints separated by gasket material, some of the energy would inevitably be lost in heat.

Another characteristic of sound or vibrational energy in structures is that the amplitude of the movement decreases as the frequency goes up. Thus at the higher frequencies the metal vibrating parts are less likely to reach their elastic limits and fail structurally. Still another characteristic of sound is that it is more easily lost in heat, in the kind of joints we have been discussing, at the higher frequencies.

Sometimes a shaft vibration can be cured by changing from a three bladed to a four or five bladed prop. This is not news to you, I am sure, but I want to warn you about mixing the cures indiscriminantly. If you have a shaft vibration problem and decide to try curing it by stiffening and breaking up the shaft, do not change the propeller to one having more blades than the old one. Breaking the shaft up raises the resonant frequency but changing the propeller can raise the exciting frequency, if the propeller happens to be at fault. The increased exciting frequency may again coincide with the increased resonant frequency of the shaft and you'll be right back where you started.

"Singing"

Singing rudders and centerboards are not usually severe problems, but they serve as an example of how to apply some of the principles of vibration to effect a cure. If the centerboard or rudder is of wood, it might be necessary only to run a couple of new bolts through them edgewise and tighten them up well. This should stiffen them and increase their resonant frequencies. If this is ineffective, it might be possible to drill some slightly undersized holes through one or more joints in the timbers making up the rudder or centerboard and drive a slightly tapered dowel into the hole in the nature of a stopwater.

Steel centerboards are difficult to stiffen because stiffening members are likely to jam in a centerboard trunk.

However, shortening the centerboard slightly will sometimes raise the resonant frequency enough to cure the singing.

It is usually a simple matter to add stiffening members to a rudder. Care should always be used in stiffening, that too much weight is not added as this tends to lower the resonant frequency and thus cancel out some of your stiffening efforts.

It is impossible to cover all the possibilities that may arise to annoy the boatowner. I have not wasted time discussing alignment of shafting and other obvious troubles because even the worst boatyard is aware of these, even though they are sometimes incapable of curing them. I have tried to outline some of the more subtle problems in the hope that when the boatowner turns to the designer in desperation, he will not do so in vain.

Acknowledgment

I owe the U.S. Navy Underwater Sound Laboratory many thanks for allowing me to extract this information from a great many reports and papers. These sources represent the efforts of a large number of engineers and scientists who either work in government laboratories or work indirectly for the government on a contract basis. This paper does not cover all phases of the noise problem because much of it is classified. It can be regarded, though, as a small additional dividend on the taxpayer's dollars if this information results in increased enjoyment of the boat-owning taxpayer.

Index

INDEX

A

Aluminum construction, 49, 192 ff.
Auxiliaries, 14

B

Buoyancy, centers of, 60 ff.

C

Colvin, Thomas E., 73, 192
Commercial boat design, 53 ff.
Conic development, 107
Conversion of a runabout, 151 ff.
Curves, dimensional and non-dimensional, 73 ff.

E

Engines, see Power Plants

F

Fiberglass construction, 36 ff.
Fishing boats, 57

G

Garden, William, 27

H

Hand, William H., 12, 13

K

Kingdom, John, 11

L

Lord, Lindsay, 19, 43, 47

M

Monocoque construction, 37, 41
Monohedron hull, 19
Motorsailers, 11 ff.
Multiconic development, 107 ff.
Munro, Gordon, 14

N

Noise suppression, 233 ff.

P

PT boats, 20
Plastic boat construction, 35 ff.
Polyester resins, 37
Power Plants, 57, 117 ff., 153, 168, 220, 235
Propellers, 115, 125, 241